HILL'S BOOK OF EVERGREENS

THE GHOST OF EVERGREEN TREE LIFE OF AGES PAST.
THE IMPERIAL, THE MAJESTIC, THE MIGHTY SEQUOIA!

Reproduced from Lawson's Pinetum Britannicum.

Hill's Book of
EVERGREENS

By L. L. KUMLIEN

Published by

D. HILL NURSERY COMPANY

DUNDEE, ILLINOIS

1936

TO MR. D. HILL (1847-1929),

PIONEER EVERGREEN GROWER, FOR NEARLY SIXTY YEARS

HEAD OF THE D. HILL NURSERY COMPANY,

THIS VOLUME IS DEDICATED

PREFACE

TWENTY YEARS of daily contact in attempting to answer the thousands of questions which people want to know about Evergreens have determined the nature of the information contained in this book.

Nothing new is claimed for the text of this book, except a new arrangement of old material, designed to meet the needs of persons not interested in the botanical or scientific study of Evergreens.

We wish to call attention to the arrangement of chapters, which are in four sections.

SECTION I. The geological and historical background, and the presentation of the families of Evergreens.

SECTION II. The cultural information; propagation, planting, pruning, etc.

SECTION III. The uses of Evergreens and the proper selection of trees for various needs.

SECTION IV. Illustrations and descriptions of the leading hardy Evergreens.

Changes are going on continually, both in the introduction of new species, particularly from Asia, the development of new varieties, as well as in the new uses which Evergreens are serving in the beautification of the landscape. Therefore, no book can ever be made that is the "last word" on the interesting subject of Evergreens.

Numerous reproductions used in this book have been made from Lawson's "Pinetum Britannicum," an English work published in 1884; Veitch's "Manual of the Coniferae," published in England in 1900; Dr. Hill's "British Herbal," an English book published in 1796; "Treatise on Planting," published by the Dublin Society in 1794; Hoopes' "Book of Evergreens," the first important American book on Evergreens, published in 1868, for which we thank the Orange Judd Publishing Company for their kind permission to make numerous plates. Our thanks are also extended to the following individuals and institutions for photographs furnished: United States National Museum; Mr. Don Glassman; Arnold Arboretum; Dr. W. M. Harlow, of the New York State College of Forestry; United States Forest Service; the late Ernest H. Wilson; the Yokohama Nursery, Yokohama, Japan; Institute of Forest Genetics; A. M. Leonard & Son; Atkins & Dubrow; Mr. Virgil Bevan; Ranier National Park Company; Park Department of Rochester, New York; Dr. L. H. Bailey; Mr. Harlan P. Kelsey; Iowa State College; Mr. George Brett; Mrs. T. B. Cook; Prof. E. I. McDaniel, of the Michigan State College; Dr. W. E. Britton, Connecticut Agricultural Experiment Station; Wisconsin Conservation Department. The other illustrations are from the files of the D. Hill Nursery Company.

CONTENTS

PART I

EVERGREENS IN GEOLOGY, FOLK LORE, HISTORY, AND POETRY

CONTENTS

PART II

SEED COLLECTING, PROPAGATION, CULTURE, DISEASES

PART III

USES OF EVERGREENS
FOUNDATION PLANTING, OUTDOOR LIVING ROOMS, HEDGES AND OTHER USES

CONTENTS

PART IV

DESCRIPTION OF VARIETIES

COLOR ILLUSTRATIONS

Part I

Evergreens in Geology, Folk Lore,
History, Poetry

CHAPTER I

Evergreens as the Geologist Sees Them

Oldest of friends, the trees!
Ere fire came, or iron,
Or the shimmering corn;
When the earth mist was dank,
Ere the promise of dawn,
From the slime, from the muck—
Trees!
—*Thomas Curtis Clark.*

THE passing of time as disclosed by the study of geology is beyond the comprehension of man. So far as meager knowledge has penetrated the mystery of the dim eternity of the past, through the discovery and classification of rock formations and the fossils contained therein, geologists have determined that the Evergreen tree, Sequoia, existed over a large part of the world more than seven million years ago! And that is but yesterday as we compute the age of the earth.

Perfectly-preserved cones, twigs, leaves and pieces of wood which have come to light in the form of fossils show that representatives of the Sequoia family, which are now making their last stand in the present state of California, formerly existed over the entire continents of North America, Europe and Asia, and even to some extent in South America. Fossils of this tree were found in Europe many years before it was discovered to be a living race of trees.

Another conifer of the most remote antiquity, which still exists in the world today, is the Bald Cypress (*Taxodium*). Almost numberless examples of genera of Evergreens now confined to some small native territory, once almost covered the land areas of the earth. Such trees as Cunninghamia, a conifer now found only in the southern hemisphere, were once a part of the North American forest. Araucarias now found in Chile were growing as far north as Greenland, along with palms, figs, magnolias and other tropical trees. Many of the species of such trees are now extinct, but some survive.

The Mesozoic age is regarded as the age of Evergreens because of the abundance and variety of species at that time. The continent of North America was low and wooded with deep forests. The outline of the land was very different

1

then than at present. The climate was much warmer, similar to southern Florida.

While we may think of the vast changes in the flora of the earth as taking place with sudden, sweeping upheaval, we know that the forces which caused the elevation of mountains, the receding of the seas, and the action of glaciers, were very likely as gradual as in our own times. We can now notice the slow disintegration of the Greenland ice cap and the gradual sinking of the seacoast in some parts of North America. Tree life, at least much of it, changed and passed away, just as the Sequoias are now on the decline. Disease perhaps wiped out entire species of trees, as the chestnuts have suffered almost complete eradication in recent years.

This is not the place to undertake even a brief outline of the ancestry of trees. It is one of the most absorbing subjects, with boundless opportunity for discovery. The piecing together of fragments of information in the study of rocks, as they are brought to light, is slowly writing the history of the past. Plant life and animal life have already been quite accurately classified according to periods or epochs. Years or centuries are not adequate terms for computing the age of trees any more than miles are of any purpose in expressing distances in astronomical calculations.

A thousand years is but the tick of the clock when we try to conceive of the ancestry of Evergreens. They were here before the mountain ranges existed, millions of years before man or any type of mammal life was on earth.

Ages of adjustment and environment have left no living trace of the strange fishes, the horrifying reptiles, and the gruesome monsters of the remote past. But Evergreens have survived! Many genera of these noble trees have clung to life through the ages. Their family lineage is supreme in all of creation.

> There rolls the deep where grew the tree.
> O earth what changes hast thou seen!
> There where the long street roars, hath been
> The stillness of the central sea.
> —*Tennyson.*

This perfectly preserved twig of a *Taxodium*, millions of years old, is almost identical with our present day *Taxodium* (Bald Cypress). Found near Spokane, Wash. Natural size. *Courtesy United States National Museum, Washington, D. C.*

A Sequoia fossil found in Miocene deposits at Salmon, Idaho. Similar fossils have been found as far north as Greenland, in Europe, Asia and in many parts of North America. Natural Size. *Photograph furnished through the courtesy of the United States National Museum, Washington, D. C.*

CHAPTER II

The Recorded History of Trees

"I will set in the desert a Fir tree and a Pine."
Isaiah 41: 19

THE beginning of knowledge and of the study of trees and plants is obscured in the dim past. Historical records lead us back only to comparatively recent times.

The interests of our ancient forebears were based almost entirely on the value of trees for medicinal purposes and for food. Trees were valued either for food, or as a source of herbs and spices.

The development of the knowledge of geography, and even the earliest beginnings of navigation, were of importance in the interchange, between nations in different parts of the world, of plants and trees. Historical information regarding the kinds of trees and plants commonly known in centuries past comes to us from a few sources of ancient culture.

What the plants of ancient Egypt were has been somewhat determined from the seeds and other evidences of tree and plant life which were preserved in the tombs of the ancient Egyptians. Many references to trees have also been found in the writings and pictures discovered of the life of the Egyptians.

Something of the plant and tree life of early Assyria and China has been preserved, and, while this information is meager, it gives many an insight to some of the interesting trees of that period. We have, of course, the mention of many sorts of trees and plant life in the Old Testament. The works of Homer contain meager reference on the subject of trees. One of the oldest of the ancient philosophers who gave some mention of plant life was Aristotle, who has been called the "Father of Natural History." Then also, we have the works of Pliny, sometimes referred to as the encyclopedist of the first century.

The Arab chiefs gave considerable time to the study of trees and plants largely for their medicinal virtues. In fact, the early interest in plants was closely interwoven with the development of the study of medicine.

During the period of the fifth to the ninth centuries, when barbarian inroads were being made over a large part of the Old World, all science and literature, including all semblance of botanical investigation, suffered. Such learning as had already been given to the world was preserved mostly by the monasteries, where manuscripts were often saved.

It was not until the beginning of the development of modern navigation that people became aware of the wealth of plant material in other parts of the world. Marco Polo and Christopher Columbus in their various voyages returned with accounts of wonderful forms of plant life which they had seen. It is true that these expeditions were strictly commercial ones, and neither Polo, Columbus, nor any of the other early explorers were interested in scientific matters. Nevertheless, observations were made which marked the beginning of the introduction of trees and plants of other shores to European countries.

It was at the beginning of the period when printing from movable type was begun, that dissemination of knowledge became more universal. Early in the history of printing, appeared two botanical books, one consisting of nineteen or twenty volumes by a Franciscan Friar, and another one several years later by a German student botanist. Other books then followed rapidly.

During this period when exploration was getting its strength, occasional plants were returned to Europe from other countries. Still nothing systematic was carried out for nearly two centuries later.

William Turner is referred to as the "Father of English Botany." He was born in 1510 and several years later produced the first English botanical work. A great deal of credit is due also to John Ray, an Englishman, who was born about 1627 and who devoted his life largely to the study of plants.

The one man in Europe who was responsible to a great extent for the modern development of botany and study of trees and plants was Linnaeus. Linnaeus had a genius for classification. During his life he proceeded to classify all forms of plant life, as well as animal life, and other divisions of natural history. Born in Sweden in 1707, he exercised a strong influence over Europe. The system that he developed for the classification of plants is the basis of our modern system of plant names.

Following Linnaeus there were many highly intellectual men throughout Europe, in Germany, Holland, France, Sweden, and England, who rapidly advanced the popular knowledge of plants. The famous Kew Gardens of England, which had their beginnings early in the seventeenth century, were responsible through their officers and associates for much of the early study and appreciation of plants from foreign countries. Through the men who were sent out by Kew many important introductions were made, not only in bringing foreign plants into England, but in transferring many native plants from foreign shores to other parts of the world. They, for instance, brought the rubber plants from Brazil to the Malay Peninsula and to India, which importation in later years was of tremendous commercial importance to the British Empire.

As has been mentioned, the study and investigation of trees and plants followed in the wake of geographical exploration. As soon as a definite route had been established around the Cape of Good Hope, taking ships from Holland,

Portugal, and England on their passage to the East Indies, the Dutch made a settlement at Capetown in 1652. Because of this settlement of civilized people, it was natural that the first plant hunter sent out by the Kew Gardens, should be sent to Capetown to make his investigations from there. Accordingly, Mr. Francis Masson was dispatched to this interesting virgin field of plant life and spent many months in the region of South Africa. It was here that were found many plants that we look upon in our daily gardening activities as having always been a part of our own landscape. Here were found such plants as the gladiolus and the freesias. In all, Masson brought back four hundred new species of plants to England, and it might be said that his success in the interest of this expedition marked the beginning of a long period of horticultural investigation.

Expeditions were organized to India, Java, and later to Australia. These early explorers, in being blown from their course around the Cape of Good Hope, had accidentally reached the shores of Australia, and in due time this continent gave up its choicest forms of trees and plants to the world.

It was not, however, until nearly two centuries after the discovery of America that professional plant hunters really came into being. The first accounts of plants in America were written by Corunti, who, in 1635, published an account of plants of America. Another Frenchman, Plumier, produced an extensive account of American plants in 1689. John Clay, an Englishman, came to Virginia in 1705, made extensive observations, published his reports, and took back with him many American plants to England. Peter Kalm, a Swedish botanist, made extensive travels in America and was really a pioneer in the scientific classification of American plant life. To the American-born John Bartram, great credit is due for establishing the first arboretum in America, and for his tireless efforts in the study of American plant life.

The nineteenth century saw the height of activity for plant hunters. By the hundreds they penetrated to the remote corners of the world until their activities are now nearly done. Mention must be made of the late Ernest Wilson, whose efforts contributed richly to the introduction of new varieties of trees and plants from many sources. Japan and China have proven to be the most productive of forms of Evergreens suitable for the northern portion of the United States and many other parts of the world. Particularly, the opening of Japan to the outside world in the early 1850's gave us the richest store of new trees suitable for the United States.

These plant hunting expeditions, which have so enriched our knowledge of the flora of other parts of the world and brought home to us the richest forms of these remote localities, were financed in different ways. First, by governments, and then by private enterprises, largely nurserymen; also by established institutions and horticultural enthusiasts. Not all of these expeditions were successful, but each contributed something toward the effort of reducing the barrier to our knowledge of plants, even to the furthermost corners of the globe.

The life of a professional plant hunter called for great physical endurance, thorough understanding of botany, and, greatest of all, patience. Even after finding a tree new to science, there remained the problem of finding a way to obtain seeds, cuttings, scions or plants, and insuring their safe arrival back home, which may have been halfway around the world. Many of these plant hunters penetrated into the back roads of far-away countries, hundreds or even thousands of miles from modern means of transportation. It is a wonder that all their specimens were not lost or destroyed before they finally reached the care of expert hands at home. The season for gathering seeds in many cases was unknown, and many visits sometimes had to be made to secure seeds at the proper season.

We are apt to think little of the origin and history of some of the interesting Evergreens which we see daily. Almost all of them have an interesting background of some sort. Some were brought with great difficulties from far away lands, and even those discovered in the early days of our own Great West were brought out with no less danger and hardship than some of the trees secured in the furthermost parts of the world.

Better acquaintance with Evergreens can be made, of course, in looking at the actual trees. Most nurseries have displays of a few sorts, and in almost every community are plantings in private grounds, or in parks, where one may make a study of varieties. Close observation will often reveal the presence of many sorts which ordinarily remain unnoticed.

Common Juniper.   *The Yew leav'd Fir.*

In one of the early works on plants, the British Herbal by Dr. Hill published in 1796 we find the above illustration of evergreens.

Chapter III

Evergreens in Religion and Folk-Lore

IN birth, in marriage, and in death, as well as on occasions of celebration, the Evergreen tree has, since time unknown, been regarded with reverence, and has been used as a symbol attending many customs.

It was an old Judean custom to plant a Cedar tree before the house on the birth of a son, and to plant a Fir tree on the birth of a daughter. These trees were regarded as sacred, never to be cut down except for building houses and furniture for those for whom the trees were planted.

The victors in the old Roman games were crowned with garlands of Pine branches as a symbol of strength and achievement. The nuts of the Stone Pine were regarded as imparting great strength and giving superior powers to the Roman warriors.

A very old custom at weddings in Bermuda was the planting of an Evergreen tree by the bride at the wedding ceremony. The cake for the wedding feast was made very high with a hole in the center, wherein a small Bermuda Cedar,

One of the largest Cedars growing on Mt. Lebanon. Frequent Biblical reference is made to the Cedars of Lebanon.

a few inches tall, was set, with the roots carefully wrapped in paper. The bride, upon making the first cut of the cake, immediately took out the young tree and planted it on a mound in front of her future home. Many of these old trees still stand today in Bermuda. The Wedding Tree in front of the Hotel Bermuda was planted on May 2, 1816, and is a familiar sight to visitors today. There are many ancestral homes in Bermuda which have one or more Wedding Trees or, as they are sometimes called, "Cake Trees."

In Japan, pictures of the Holy Pine, with its double stem, are presented to every bride and groom on their wedding day.

Our Pilgrim forefathers were so thankful to see the green forests of New England which were to furnish them fuel, shelter, and other comforts, that they chose the Pine tree to adorn their first coins, the Pine Tree Shillings. Today, in the State of Maine, the Pine Tree State, the Pine branch is the State flower.

Persisting even until our own day, is the use at funerals of the Cypress and the Yew branches. Thus, from the beginning of life to the very end, we find Evergreens associated with human life.

The worship of trees is one of the oldest forms of divine reverence. In ancient mythology, down through the heathen religions to our present Christianity, we find a great reverence for trees. This is not so hard to understand when we come to realize that it was the custom of ancient people to worship sources of natural benefits, such as the heat of the sun, the moon, etc. Trees were often looked upon as the abode of the spirits and were raised as sacred objects. It has long been a source of conjecture and unusual coincidence, that the Scandinavian conception of the origin of the human race coincides with that legend held by the American Algonquin Indians; namely, that man was created from a tree.

So far back as human records have been found, six thousand years ago in the writings of the Chaldeans, we find references to trees and pictures, which accounts indicate the respect in which trees were held.

In the ancient paintings and sculpture of Assyria, are many symbols of tree-worship.

The Date Palm, the Cedar, the Pine, and the Fig particularly were considered as sources of strength for the gods. The modern Mohammedan still pays great honor to trees.

The prophet Isaiah seeking to illustrate the benevolence of the Lord, makes reference to the Evergreen as a symbol of abundance and comfort. "I will plant in the Wilderness the Cedar. I will set in the desert the Fig tree and the Pine." Evergreens have been looked upon with great respect for their enduring qualities. "The voice of the Lord breaketh the Cedar of Lebanon"; so wrote a Biblical writer, and his figure of speech concedes it was the strongest power the imagination of that day could offer.

In India, where worship of heathen gods was a common practice, there are hundreds of legends handed down for thousands of years. The Tree of ten thousand Images was the mecca of many travelers. The legend of this tree was associated with the early life of an Indian boy who, in his mature years, became Buddha.

It is not surprising that many of these old customs and superstitions should hold over, undergoing some changes, of course, into the Christian era. It was then that spirits, goblins, and witches were thought to inhabit certain trees. It was then, also, that great reverence developed for certain trees in the vicinity of which great deeds were done or miracles performed. As late as the twelfth century the canons of the churches in England and Ireland rebelled against too much reverence for sacred trees, and church followers were urged to break away from this heathen practice.

There have been, since the crucifixion of Christ, innumerable legends concerning the tree from which the cross of crucifixion was made. Many of these superstitions persist until the present day.

While we look upon the worship of trees as a long-past practice, there still exist today many examples of tree-worship. In Arabia, for instance, the tribesmen always pray under a certain variety of tree. In the Congo a holy tree is planted before each village house, with jars of wine provided for spirit offerings. In New Guinea are sacred trees which one must not touch under peril of death. In sections of Africa, women are occasionally designated by tribal chiefs to wait upon certain trees and spend their entire time looking after the imaginary wants of these trees.

As common and well-loved an institution as the Maypole Dance has its origin in ancient times when it was the custom to dance about in jubilation around some tree for the supposed benefit of the wood-spirits.

The first Christmas tree was a living Fir tree. According to the old legend, Saint Winifred, a missionary in the eighth century, eager to turn the minds of the Druids from the worship of the sun, moon, and thunder, begged them to become worshippers of a living God, but still they clung to their old ritual. He dramatically chose the moment when they were gathered at the foot of the monstrous oak sacred to the god of thunder. Suddenly, so the story goes, the missionary gave a signal to his woodsmen to cut the oak tree. The great oak, symbol of a dead god, fell to the ground, and in the clearing the people were astonished to see a living Fir tree, young, beautiful, and strong. The missionary, joyous at being able to put the worship of life into the hearts of his followers, said, "Here is the living tree that shall be the sign of your new worship." And so the Evergreen tree has become our symbol of love and peace at the Christmas season.

Many of the religious and social customs of ancient people are revolting to us, but in tree worship we usually find nothing but beauty. As we look upon the grace and the nobility of a tree, it is not hard for us to imagine that we ourselves might partake somewhat of the spirit of worship which people of ancient times carried on.

> "I care not how men trace their ancestry,
> To ape or Adam: let them please their whim;
> But I in June am midway to believe
> A tree among my fair progenitors."
> —*James Russell Lowell*

The spreading glory of the Cypress del Tule—colossus of the floral kingdom. Surviving civilizations, conquests, revolutions—it has outlived every span. It is the consensus of opinion among botanists and archeologists that El Tule, as the tree is generally known, is the oldest living thing on the earth.

Three, five, or ten thousand years ago the seed of a cypress rooted in the ground at Oaxaca, Mexico, where the village of Santa Maria del Tule now stands, and grew into a colossus of the floral kingdom.

This robust child of nature lives within a fenced enclosure and beside a deserted Catholic Church colored in bright red, white, and blue. The San Felipe range of mountains rises up in the distance and completes a setting that is unforgettable.

Following the sinuosities of El Tule's gigantic trunk, one measures its perimeter as 108 feet at a height of five feet above the ground. So far as is known, no organism ever attained such a vast girth. But El Tule's girth is out of all proportion to its height of 141 feet which is surpassed by trees in more temperate climates.

The outline of El Tule's canopy is plump and quite spherical. It throws a ground shadow with an area of 7,200 square feet when the sun is at its zenith, enough for a small army to shelter beneath its spreading branches. Indeed, it is rumored that none other than Hernan Cortez and his army camped there, on the march to Honduras.

—*Don Glassman*

CHAPTER IV

Poetical Tributes to Evergreens

THERE is an elusive quality in old Evergreens, an appeal to sentiment and imagination, which has inspired many poetical expressions of praise for these noble trees. One of the most soothing melodies of nature is heard in the musical whisperings of the pines. In their steadfastness, their solitude, their rugged strength, their majestic beauty, and their abiding peace, we feel a certain reverence. They grow old but are forever young. The selections which follow are but a few of many poetical tributes to the glory of Evergreens.

"Make me a home in the forest,
    Where its shadows linger deep—
Where truth shall know my spirit,
And the pines their vigil keep."
                        —*Harry T. Fee.*

THE WOOING

Two cedars, twins,
Danced with the winds,
Who sang them ardent pleas;
    The Frost lads came
    And wooed the same
Two slender cedar trees.
                —*Whitelaw Saunders.*

HAIL, KINDLY CEDARS! HAIL!

Oh, here's a glee to the cedars,
    Our stanch old friends and true!
What boots the snow, when the wild winds
        blow;
For never a change do the cedars know
    All the long years through.
                —*William Frederick Held.*

The pine tree is our own tree,
A grown tree, a cone tree,
The tree to face a bitter wind,
The tree for mast and spar—
A mounting tree, a fine tree,
A fragrant turpentine tree,
A limber tree, a timber tree,
And resinous with tar.
                —*Christopher Morley.*

"In fact, there's nothing that keeps its youth,
so far as I know, but a tree, and truth."
                —*Oliver Wendell Holmes.*

TO A TIMBERLINE TREE

"Crippled and bent by eternal blasts
Winning life's battle by holding fast
To your place in the world as it was ordained.
Timberline Tree, I am so ashamed
Of the fight I've made in the world of men;
I go back to the valley to fight again."
　　　　　—Charles Bowman Hutchins.

　　　　　　　No refrain
Is sweeter than the night-winds lay among
　　The fragrant pines, no choir's swelling voice
Is deeper, more exalting than the song
　　Of roaring surf, or distant thunder's noise,
Heard in the forest evergreen—while long
　　And loud in primal tones they do rejoice.
　　　　　—Leslie Burroughs.

THE ETERNAL PINE

The centuries came, the centuries went,
　　Harsh despots ruled and brave men fought,
Kingdoms were born and kingdoms spent,
　　Knowledge and truth great sages sought.
Through all the rack of human strife,
　　The storm-king's blast or lightning's flame,
'Mid evil, good; throughout my life
　　Serene I stood, whatever came.

High on a hill a goodly cedar grewe,
Of wondrous length and straight proportion,
That farre abroad her dainte odours threwe;
'Mongst all the daughters of proud Lebanon
Her match in beauty was not anie one.
　　　　　　　　　　—Spenser.

Under the yaller pines I house,
　　When sunshine makes them all sweet scented.
An' hear among their furry boughs
　　The baskin' west wind purr contented.
　　　　　　　　　　—Lowell.

I OWN A PINE TREE

Today a lawyer handed me a deed,
Full of descriptive terms and legal lore;
Replete with words I never heard before,
All stupid stuff, I do not care to read.
I gather from its text that I agreed
To have and hold, till time shall be no more,
A lot. But why should its contents ignore
The pine tree, that, to me, was thus decreed?
　　　　　　—Margaret Wheeler Ross.

The delicate tracery of twig and bough
Stands revealed against winter's frosty sky.
Brings us the airs of hills and forest,
The sweet aroma of birch and pine;
Give us a waft of the north wind laden
With sweet brier odors and breath of kine.
　　　　　　　　　　—Whittier.

THE SINGING LEAVES

But the trees all kept their council
And never a word said they,
Only there sighed from the pine tops
A music of seas far away.
　　　　　　　　　　—Lowell.

THE PINE TREE

Regal and stately behold it stand
Above its brethren, towering grand,
A sentinel guarding the sleeping land.
   Beauty and grace in its form combine,
   A monarch, born of a noble line,
   Long may it be, ere its race decline!
   Frost shall not wither a leaf of thine,
      Fearless and fadeless Pine!
           —Mary F. Tucker.

I can hear the outdoors calling;—
   See the forest, red and gold,
Where the autumn streams are brawling
   Over pebbles, clear and cold.
I can see the river flowing
   Past the oaks and fragrant pines—
Back to nature I am going,
   While the Hunter's Moon still shines!
      —Clarence Mansfield Lindsay.

Transfused through you, O mountain friends!
With mine your solemn spirit blends,
And life no more hath separate ends;
I read each misty mountain sign,
I know the voice of wave and pine
And I am yours and ye are mine.
Life's burdens fall, its discords cease,
I lapse into the glad release
Of Nature's own exceeding peace.

        —Whittier.

One little hour to lie unseen
Beneath thy scarf of leafy green!
So, curtained by a singing Pine,
Its murmuring voice shall blend with mine,
Till, lost in dreams, my faltering lay
In sweeter music dies away.
      —Oliver Wendell Holmes.

You may as well forbid the mountain pines
To wag their high tops, and to make no noise
When they are fretted with the gusts of heaven.
      —Shakespeare.

I remember, I remember,
The Fir trees dark and high;
I used to think their slender tops
Were close against the sky:
It was a childish ignorance,
But now 'tis little joy
To know I'm farther off from heaven
Than when I was a boy.
                    —*Thomas Hood.*

THE HARPS AND THE EVERGREEN CHILDREN

To each of the Evergreen children
    There is brought at the hour of its birth
A magic, sweet harp, as I fancy,
    For the little tree's dower on earth
And at twilight is planted by fairies
    By the side of each wee baby tree
And they grow there all summer together
    Tho' the harps you and I may not see.
                    —*Leander Goetz.*

O Hemlock tree! O Hemlock tree! how
    faithful are thy branches!
    Green not alone in summertime,
    But in the winter's frost and rime!
O Hemlock tree! O Hemlock tree! how
    faithful are thy branches!
                    —*Longfellow.*

THE CYPRESS

I saw a bent and ancient tree,
A withered cypress by the sea,
Its leafless arms were black as night
Against the flaming sunset light.
And grace incarnate rested there
In quiet beauty, strange and fair.
To some, it was an ugly thing,
And marred the loveliness of Spring.
But I—I thanked the loving God
Who put that cypress in the sod.
                    —*Mary S. Hawling.*

PINES

Pines, Pines, why do you murmur
Rimes, rimes, runic and quaint?
Pines, Pines, your sad susurrous
Makes our fond hearts to grow faint.
O Pines, darkling Pines,
What is your mystical plaint?

Blow, blow, O gentle zephyrs,
Breathe low, soft melody;—
Wave, wave, evergreen Druids,
Waft the weird strain to the sky.
Pines, Pines, solemn Pines,
What do ye prophesy?
                    —*J. B. Nykerk.*

CALL OF THE PINES

When—where I stand
Seems poor and loose and sandy;
When, for my song,
I'd substitute a whine;
When loaded down with tears
Or toil, I waver—
Come, Wind of God,
And play upon a pine.
—*John D. Clinton.*

What is the secret the pine-trees know
That keeps them whispering, soft and low?
All day long in the breezes swaying,
What can it be they are always saying?
—*Jennie G. Clarke.*

As sunbeams stream through liberal space
And nothing jostle or displace,
So waves the pine-tree through my thought
And fanned the dreams it never brought.
—*Emerson.*

Beneath the forest's skirts I rest,
　　Whose branching Pines rise dark and
　　　high,
And hear the breezes of the West,
　　Among the thread-like foliage sigh.
—*Bryant.*

Cedar, and pine, and fir, and branching
　　palm,
A sylvan scene, and as the ranks ascend
Shade above shade, a woody theatre
Of statliest view.
—*Milton.*

SNOWFALL

Snow has blown down
From the wings of night;
Trees grow majestic
Under their ermine.

The young spruce is a princess
Carved in alabaster and ebony.
The little plum tree
Is a Japanese print in black and white.

The giant pines are
Two stout countesses
Heavily burdened with
Long white ermine.

—*Alice Lenore.*

JUST A BATTERED OLD TREE

The Timberline Tree is not beautiful, if you look for beauty in symmetry, and lush foliage, and graceful lines. At times the battle has gone against it, and the marks of many a defeat are plain to be seen.

Up where all the other trees have abandoned the unequal fight, the Timberline Tree holds the farthest outpost of life. I know that the Timberline Tree is not good for fruit, nor is it of much material use to the children of men. But its spirit is that of the adventurer, who goes far beyond any chances of gain or glory, and shows what intrepidity can compass. I think of it as in some way kin to the Lincolns among men.

And I think of One who bowed his head against bitterer winds than have beat on all the sons of men, but who stood his ground until the day when he could say, "In the world ye shall have tribulation; but be of good cheer. I have overcome the world!"

—*Justus Timberline.*

CHAPTER V

Botanical Names and Pronunciation

BOTANICAL names are often a bugbear to amateur horticulturists. The names have unfamiliar sounds and combinations of letters. Nevertheless, botanical names will always be with us. They are a necessary evil. Anyone who does not believe in the need of botanical names has but to turn to "Check List of the Forest Trees of the United States" by Sudworth. Here he will find twenty, and even thirty, local, common names applied to the same tree in different localities. Even the use of botanical names does not eliminate all confusion. There are different opinions among those versed in horticultural nomenclature.

Botanical names are in Latin, or, if derived from some other language, are expressed in the Latinized form. An interesting diversion awaits anyone with an inclination to study the derivation of plant names. Few of us in this modern day possess either the necessary ready acquaintance with classical Greek and Latin or the patience to explore the subject intimately.

While botanical names are confusing when viewed as a mass of unrelated words, they are not so formidable as they seem, for they all tell a story of some kind.

The advantage of using names in Latin and classical Greek, languages which are no longer in common use, lies in the fact that these languages are not subject to change. They also have the advantage of being understood by scientific men of all nationalities throughout the world.

The older names of some of the families of Evergreens come to us from ancient times. The original meanings are either unknown or cannot be affirmed. The name "Abies," for instance, is thought to be derived from both Latin and Greek words meaning "a pear," having to do with the shape of the tree. The meanings of many of the older names are not clearly understood.

Some of the other names are not difficult to trace. Generally they are found to express some peculiar characteristic of the tree. The name "Callitris," for instance, is derived from the Greek, meaning "beauty" and "thrice," a reference to the whorl of leaves which are in threes. The name "Dacrydium" comes from the Greek word meaning "tear," alluding no doubt to an unusual weeping or shedding of gum. The Libocedrus takes its name from "frankincense" and "cedar," a remarkable fragrance particularly noticeable to the botanist who first named the tree.

Other families of Evergreens have been named in honor of some individual. The Sequoia, for instance, bears the name of a half-breed Cherokee Indian who originated the Cherokee alphabet.

Species of Evergreens often bear proper names, such as: Pseudotsuga *douglasi* and Picea *engelmanni,* named in honor of David Douglas and Dr. Engelmann.

Some names are based on natural habitat, such as: Pinus *palustris*—marsh-loving; Pinus *maritima*—from the seashore; or Pinus *sylvestris*—forest-loving.

Geographical names: Juniperus *japonica*—from Japan; and Larix *europea*—from Europe.

Names based on color, such as: Pinus *strobus*—the White Pine; Picea *rubra*—the Red Spruce; and Pinus *nigra*—the Black Pine.

Names based on some peculiarity of the tree, such as: Juniperus *monosperma*—single-seeded; Juniperus *macrocarpa*—long fruited; or Abies *brachyphylla*—short leaved.

Names exalting the tree, such as: Abies *grandis*—grand or noble; and Pinus *insignis*—unusual.

Names used in describing individual varieties almost invariably try to describe the outstanding characteristic of the variety. Thus, we have recurring frequently in the names of horticultural varieties such descriptive terms as the following, referring to characteristics of foliage, habit, cones, or color:

Alba—white	Glauca—bluish
Argentea—silver	Globosa—globe
Aurea—golden	Nana—dwarf
Compacta—close-growing	Pendula—weeping
Conica—cone-shaped	Prostrata—low, spreading
Dumosa—bushy	Pumila—low or little
Erecta—upright	Pyramidalis—pyramidal
Fastigiata—pyramidal or sentinel	Repens—creeping
Filiform—thread-like	Viridis—green

Many of these descriptive terms are so closely related to our usual English words that there is little difficulty in guessing the meaning. On the other hand, many terms have been applied promiscuously by persons without proper understanding of the use of such terms, and this has resulted in many misapplied names.

If a name is once understood and associated with a tree, it is not so difficult to remember.

By referring to a dictionary of botanic terms the meaning of botanical terms will be greatly simplified.

How to Pronounce Names of Evergreens

Because they are only occasionally used, the names of Evergreens, both botanical and common, are not so familiar. In some instances there is more than one accepted form of pronunciation. Almost all of these names will be found in any good standard dictionary, but for convenience we have listed the names of the important genera of Evergreens, and also some of the common names and other terms. The authority quoted is Webster's New International Dictionary. Key to pronunciation is as follows:

ā as in ale	ĕ as in end	ŏ as in soft
ȧ as in senate	ĕ as in recent	ŏ as in connect
â as in care	ē as in maker	ū as in use
ă as in am	ī as in ice	û as in unite
ă as in account	ĭ as in ill	û as in urn
ä as in arm	ō as in old	ŭ as in up
ȧ as in ask	ŏ as in obey	ŭ as in circus
ȧ as in sofa	ô as in orb	ü as in menu
ē as in eve	ōō as in too	
ê as in event	ŏ as in odd	

Evergreen Terms

Abies (ā′bĭ-ēz)
Araucaria (ăr′ô-kā′rĭ-ȧ)
Arborvitae (är′bŏr-vī′tē)
Cedrus (sē′drŭs)
Cephalotaxus (sĕf′ȧ-lŏ-tăk′sŭs)
Chamaecyparis (kăm′ē-sĭp′ȧ-rĭs)
conifer (kō′nĭ-fēr)
Cryptomeria (krĭp′tŏ-mē′rĭ-ȧ)
Cunninghamia (kŭn′ĭngham′ĭ-ȧ)
Cupressus (kṵ-prĕs′ŭs)
Cypress (sī′prĕs)
fir (fûr)
genus (jē′nŭs) (Singular)
genera (jĕn′ē-rȧ) (Plural)
juniper (jōō′nĭ-pēr)
Juniperus (jōō-nĭp′ēr-ŭs)
Larix (lār′ĭks)

Libocedrus (lī′bŏ-sē′drŭs)
Picea (pĭs′ē-ȧ)
Pinus (pī′nŭs)
Podocarpus (pŏd′ô-kär′pŭs)
Pseudotsuga (sū′dŏ-tsū′gȧ)
Retinispora (rĕt′ĭ-nĭs′pŏ-rȧ)
Sciadopitys (sī′ȧ-dŏp′ĭ-tĭs)
Sequoia (sē-kwoi′ȧ)
species (spē′shēz)
spruce (sprōōs)
Taxodium (tăk-sō′dĭ-ŭm)
Taxus (tăk′sŭs)
Thuya (thū′yȧ)
Thuyopsis (thṵ-yŏp′sĭs)
Torreya (tŏr′ĭ-ȧ)
Tsuga (tsū′gȧ)
yew (yōō)

CHAPTER VI

Color in Evergreens

OF the six fundamental colors of the solar spectrum, the foliage of evergreen trees displays green, yellow, and blue. The orange, red, and violet colors are also seen, but only in the buds, the flowers, the cones, or the bark. To say that evergreens are of monotonous color is an admission of careless observation. On the other hand, it is true that the greatest variety of colors in nature is reserved for other forms of plant life. Unfortunately, but few people correctly appreciate variations of color; much less do they distinguish color variation by name. Therefore, descriptive terms regarding color are almost useless, other than simple terms such as light green or dark green.

When we consider that one standard reference on color nomenclature names and illustrates 1115 distinct colors, we gain some idea of the striking lack of appreciation, among most people, of fine shadings of colors. To be sure, life is too crowded with more important things for us ever to hope to become color experts. However, the development of a closer observation of the beautiful and delicate gradations of greens, blues, and yellows will greatly increase our enjoyment of the marvelous handiwork of nature, as she freshens the new, unfolding buds, darkens the matured leaves or needles, and at last tints them again with the touch of autumn.

On many species, the underside of the needle is in different color than the upperside. Generally, such needles are bluish beneath, sometimes having one or more fine white lines running the length of the needles.

Watch the verdant, green new needles of the Larch. See how they darken as the season progresses until they change to the pale gold of autumn. This tree is one of the deciduous conifers (which lose their leaves in winter). Most evergreens in the temperate zone have three distinct color changes a year: the color of the new season's growth, the color of the summer growing season, and the color of fall and winter.

In golden or yellow varieties of evergreens, some are bright yellow in the spring, when the new growth develops, and gradually darken during the season—Douglas Golden Arborvitae and Golden Prostrate Juniper, for example. Others start out green and develop the golden tint in the fall. A familiar subject is the Goldtip Redcedar.

Blue evergreens, of which there is a large number, show many shades of blue, which vary by species and also by seasons and differ materially in their tones, from whitish blue to deeper shades of gray. Much of the color of blue ever-greens, such as the familiar Blue Spruce, is not a pigment in the leaf itself, but a bloom or sheen, such as we find on grapes and plums. It can be rubbed off with the fingers, and, therefore, is oftentimes lost by the effect of snow and winter storms, to return again with the new growth in the spring.

Many horticultural varieties owe their existence to some peculiar color habit. The Andorra Juniper, for example, is bright green when making its new season's growth, changes to a grayish-green summer color, and then undergoes a complete change of wardrobe for fall and winter, the color of which might be accurately described as dull magenta purple. A somewhat similar phenome-non takes place in the Dundee Juniper, whose winter color is still a different purplish hue. Many examples might be given of the striking changes that evergreens undergo in completely changing color.

In the majority of species, the change of color is from one shade of green to another. Because of the limitations of commonly-understood descriptive terms of color, we can only hope to direct closer attention and urge your personal observation throughout the year to gain the greatest enjoyment of your ever-greens. It is not too far a stretch of imagination to say that *no two species or varieties of evergreens are exactly the same color.*

It is not only in difference of color, but in texture of foliage that evergreens offer variety. Even though the colors are quite similar, the delicate needles of the Hemlock give a vastly different effect than some coarse-needled Pine.

OTHER COLOR VARIATIONS

The new shoots of evergreens, when brought to closer observation, disclose remarkable differences in color. Some are downy or hairy; others, smooth. Some are brownish, some reddish, some gray, some yellow, some purplish or blue, and some olive green. We suggest that you will be greatly surprised if you examine some new shoots next spring.

COLOR IN CONES

The most vivid shades of color in evergreens are found in the cones, par-ticularly in the early stages of development. The richest gold and purple and crimson are all there if you look for them. Some are studded with shiny beads of resin which sparkle like jewels. If you want to surprise your friends with a most unusual bouquet, cut a few evergreen cones. And do not forget the powdery blue berries of the Junipers, cut with a spray of deep green foliage, or the crimson Yew berries with their almost black-green needles. Bring such a bouquet into the house. No color in evergreens? Nothing but somber green? You may as well say there is no color in a sunset.

Color in Trunks

Even the trunks of older evergreens exhibit interesting characteristics. The Lace Bark Pine of China, upon reaching the age of fifty years, undergoes a transfiguration and assumes a white bark, at first with patches of white, and gradually a full creamy-white covering. The bark of the Cork Bark Fir, or Arizona Fir, in its old age also turns white and produces a bark of spongy cork. Some trunks are smooth; others, deeply fissured. If you look, you will see color there, too—maybe gray, or brown, or the soft, red color of an old violin.

> Trunks of trees in a deep, deep wood:
>   In that fern-lit dusk they loom—
>   Massive cedar, hemlock, spruce—
>   Silver shafts against the gloom;
> Fathom their beauty no man could:
> Lonely trunks in a deep, deep wood.
>
> Trunks of trees against the sky:
>   Dark they rise, in curveless grace,
>   Straight they cut the sky behind
>   Into many a panelled space:
> Nor man nor book can satisfy
> Like trunks of trees against the sky.
>
>   —*Olga Weydemeyer*

CHAPTER VII

Some Foliage Characteristics in Evergreens

PERSISTENCE OF LEAVES

WE are apt to make a distinction between Evergreen trees and leaf-bearing trees by thinking that Evergreens never shed their needles, and that other kinds of trees drop their leaves with the coming of frost in the fall. This popular misconception is no doubt due to the fact that most Evergreens do not shed *all of their leaves* at once. The shedding process goes on gradually and is less noticeable. Every one who has been in the forest knows, of course, that the forest floor is made up largely of the needles which are shed each year.

There are exceptions to this rule, even in the Evergreen family. The Larch sheds all of its needles in the fall and grows new leaves each spring. The same is true of the Bald Cypress.

In some families of Evergreens, Arborvitae for example, all of the foliage, when it becomes two years old, turns brown and drops off early in the fall. This condition is frequently viewed with alarm by persons who mistake this normal process for an unhealthy condition. When the fall season is dry, this browning seems to occur more suddenly. In other years the process is more gradual and less noticeable.

In the case of the Arborvitae referred to, the needles which develop one spring, stay on the tree during that year and shed at the end of the second summer. In this way there are always two season's growth of needles on the tree at the same time.

We quote some remarks concerning the persistence of Evergreen leaves from "Revision of Genus Pinus" by Dr. George Engelmann:

"The persistence of the leaves is very different in different species; in White Pine and others, they fall in the autumn of the second year. More commonly they last to the end of the third year; in some species, Jack Pine, they do not fall until they are four, five, or six years old. In some varieties, I have seen them exist twelve to fourteen years."

From the above quotation it will readily be seen why there is often such a difference in the density of the needles among various species of Evergreens.

25

The shedding of needles, which we have described, is a natural and normal process in the life of an Evergreen tree. They do, however, sometimes shed some of their needles when they have suffered a severe shock.

When Evergreens become very dry on the roots, some of the needles will usually drop off—perhaps on the lower branches. The tree strives to maintain all of its needles, but, when there is a shortage of moisture, enough needles will fall to balance up for the required amount of moisture. Seldom will an Evergreen lose all of its needles and still recover. It is possible, however, for a tree to grow again if the buds are healthy and the tree has a favorable opportunity.

An individual branch which has been injured will dry up and lose its needles. When the wood is dry and brittle, no amount of nursing will bring it back to life. Application of liquid manure, as described under "Fertilizer" in this book, will often bring back to life trees which are apparently too far gone for recovery.

Foliage Differences

Among the twenty-four families of Evergreens enumerated in this book, there is a vast field for interesting study of foliage characteristics. However, as this book is not intended for scientific research, but only as a source of popular information, we must be content to limit our observations to a glimpse or two at some interesting aspects of the foliage or needles of a few more common families of Evergreens, such as are usually grown in the vicinity of Chicago.

Needles of the Pines

The needles of Pines are borne in clusters, the grouping in different species ranging from 1 to 5.

The One-Leaf Pine

The Single-leaf Pine (*Pinus monophylla*), an American species, has but a single needle in a cluster, growing one inch to one and three-fourths inches long.

The Two-Leaved Pines

This group contains twenty or more species, all of which bear needles in groups of two. Some well known Pines in this group are:

		Length
Jack Pine (Pinus banksiana)	1	to 1¾ inches
Scotch Pine (Pinus sylvestris)	2	to 3 inches
Japanese Red Pine (Pinus densiflora)	3	to 4 inches
Red Pine (Pinus resinosa)	5	to 6½ inches
Austrian Pine (Pinus nigra)	3	to 5 inches

The Three-Leaved Pines

This is an extensive group including several familiar American species, a few of which are as follows:

Length

Coulter Pine (Pinus coulteri)	8 to 12 inches
Western Yellow Pine (Pinus ponderosa) . . .	8 to 12 inches
Pitch Pine (Pinus rigida)	3½ to 4½ inches
Longleaf Pine (Pinus palustris)	7 to 18 inches

The Four-Leaved Pine

The Parry Pine (*Pinus parryana*) of California bears a cluster of four leaves (occasionally 5) growing 1¼ to 1½ inches long.

The Five-Leaved Pines

This group is composed of about twenty species and bears its needles in clusters of five. Among this group are several familiar trees whose average length of needles in inches is indicated below:

Length

Bhotan Pine (Pinus excelsa)	5 to 8 inches
Sugar Pine (Pinus lambertiana)	3½ to 4 inches
White Pine (Pinus strobus)	3 to 4 inches
Swiss Stone Pine (Pinus cembra)	1½ to 3½ inches
Limber Pine (Pinus flexilis)	2½ to 3 inches

The needles of most Pines are three-sided. They show various minute characteristics in the formation of the needle. Some are sharp-pointed on the end; some, rounded. The sides of the needle may be smooth or jagged. Some are flexible, soft, and pendulous; others, stiff. Some are twisted and some straight. The surfaces of some species are concave. Some have one ridge or several ridges. Some are very fine and delicate; others, thick and coarse. Some have an aromatic odor; others do not. Variations in the same species are not unusual. When you speak of a "Pine needle," you are covering a mighty big territory. After considering Pine needles briefly, you can perhaps better appreciate why a nurseryman, or even a learned botanist, can not always identify a Pine when you hand him a cluster of needles.

The Needles of the Firs

This may be a good place to make an explanation of the botanical terms, ABIES (Fir) and PICEA (Spruce). The earliest writers on Evergreens thus distinguished these two great Evergreen families. Later, the great Swedish botanist, Linnaeus, who lived in the 18th century, and who undertook to classify and name all plant life, reversed these names. For many years thereafter it was customary to refer to Spruce as *Abies* and Firs as *Picea*. Hemlock (*Tsuga*) was also called *Abies*. Thus we find, in many old books on Evergreens, a confusion of names. Some writers followed one system; some, another. During the 19th century, however, most writers reverted to the original system of naming *Picea* as Spruces and *Abies* as Firs. This system is now almost universally used.

An easily-understood difference between Firs and Spruces is the manner in which the needles are attached to the shoot or branchlet. Fir needles, when they fall, or are detached, leave a circular depression nearly smooth, and flush with the surface of the branchlet as shown in figure 1. By referring to figure 5 (page 29), under the explanation of Spruces, this marked characteristic difference will be easily seen.

Fir needles persist and do not fall when the branch is cut off and becomes dry. Spruce needles drop very quickly. This feature accounts for the preference given to Firs for cut Christmas trees.

The surest means of identifying Firs is from the cones, which stand erect. Spruce cones hang down. The scales of the Fir cones drop off when the seeds are released. The cone actually falls apart, leaving only the stem of the cone remaining on the tree. Spruce cones release their seed but retain the scales of the cone.

Fir needles are fragrant; some, more fragrant than others. This fragrance is more noticeable when the needles are crushed. Spruce needles, on the contrary, have a strong odor not pleasant to the smell.

Compared to Spruces, the Fir foliage is soft and flexible to the touch. Spruce

Fig. 1   Fig. 2   Fig. 3

Fig. 5

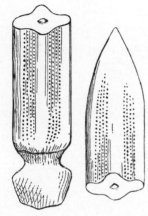

Fig. 4

needles are stiff and sharp. Like some other families, most Fir needles are silver-lined. Some are very light blue on the reverse of the leaf, making a beautiful sight when the branches move in the breeze.

Fir needles are not borne in clusters, as in the Pine family, but each needle is fastened separately to the branch.

The actual leaf-arrangement of Fir needles must be carefully examined to notice that while the needles *appear* to grow only out of the sides and sometimes the top of the shoot, they *actually* grow from entirely around the stem and are then twisted into two or more rows of needles along the stem. This peculiar characteristic is shown in figures 2 and 3.

Many of the Firs are lustrous, shiny, or waxy, as if they had been highly polished. Many have a bluish-green color; some, yellow-green, and others, very deep, dark green.

THE NEEDLES OF THE SPRUCES

Spruces are particularly difficult to distinguish one from another. There is a close resemblance between many different species, and they also are quite variable, especially in cultivation. It is not so difficult, however, to identify Spruces, as a family, from other genera of conifers.

Their needles are borne singly, and they are more or less four-sided. (See cross-section of leaf, figure 4.) There are some few exceptions to this characteristic, as will be explained.

The needles are arranged radially; that is, entirely around the stem, except for a few species which closely resemble Firs in their foliage arrangement.

All Spruces have an identifying mark. As shown in figure 5, the needles are attached to the branchlet by a woody, raised projection. The needle cannot be removed without tearing away a small piece of the bark or rind. When branches are cut and the needles drop off, or when they drop naturally, they leave the little projection, or scar, as shown in figure 5. This characteristic is a main point of difference between Spruces and Firs.

The cones of Spruce, when matured, are not erect. They generally hang downward or nearly so. Firs, on the other hand, hold their cones erect.

Leaves of Spruce are almost invariably stiff and sharp-pointed, as compared to the Firs. Also, there is a marked point of difference in the odor of the crushed needles. Firs are pungent and often very fragrant; Spruces have a strong, and sometimes disagreeable, odor.

Needles of the Junipers

Aside from the division of Juniper foliage as either juvenile or adult, there is but little help for amateur observers in distinguishing Junipers by foliage characteristics alone.

The foliage of Junipers is of two distinct kinds: the sharp-pointed, prickly needles, and the scale-like, whipcord formation. The prickly needles may predominate in one tree; the scale-like needles in another tree. Both kinds frequently appear on the same tree, either permanently or in the transitional stage.

Identification of Junipers, therefore, is reduced mostly to a consideration of the color of the foliage and the habit of the tree. Because of characteristic differences in this regard, it is necessary to become familiar with shapes and colors as described elsewhere in this book under "Description of Varieties," pages 210 to 236.

However, Junipers may be easily distinguished from other genera of Evergreens if they are found with berries. Figure 6 shows a branch of Redcedar (*Juniperus virginiana*) with berries and adult, or scale-like leaves. In figure 7 the juvenile, or prickly foliage is shown.

Fig. 6   *Fig. 7*

NEEDLES OF THE ARBORVITAES

We quote from Ruskin's "Modern Painters" a great American author's description of the formation of the Arborvitae foliage: "In the Arborvitae there is no proper stem to the outer leaves, but all the extremities form a sort of corraline leaf, flat and fernlike, which gradually concentrates and embraces itself into the stem. The thicker branches of the tree are exquisitely fantastic; and the mode in which the flat system of leaf first produces an irregular branch and then adapts itself to the symmetrical cone of the whole tree is one of the most interesting processes of form which I know in vegetation."

Many variations occur in the Arborvitae family in the horticultural varieties, both as to the color of the leaves and the shape of the leaves. Some forms are golden; some, white-tipped. The leaves of some are crested or slightly twisted.

As in the families of Junipers, Cypress, Arborvitaes and some others, the baby, or juvenile foliage is of a different character than the older, or adult foliage. See figure 8. In some horticultural varieties of Arborvitae the juvenile foliage never matures, so that the trees do not resemble their normal type.

While there is little difficulty in identifying Arborvitae as a family when they carry the normal foliage, there are certain trees among the other genera of Evergreens such as Cypress, Chamaecyparis, and Junipers, which closely resemble Arborvitae. When cones may be observed, there is no question; because the cones of Junipers are in the form of berries, the Cypress is a rounded knob (see figure 9), and the Arborvitae has a still different cone.

There is a pungent odor which is alone characteristic of the Arborvitae.

Fig. 9

Fig. 10. Foliage of Arborvitae one-half natural size.

Fig. 8

Needles of the Hemlocks

In the earlier efforts of classifying Evergreens, the Hemlock was the "wandering Jew" of the conifer family. At first included in Pines, later in Firs, and also in the Spruce tribe, it was finally, in quite recent times, given a family name or genus of its own, *Tsuga*. It was thus named by the French botanist, Carriere. It is still sometimes referred to as "Hemlock Spruce" or "Hemlock Fir."

It bears close relation in many details to other families of Evergreens. Its cones resemble Larch. The leaves look like the leaves of a miniature Fir, but resemble the Spruces in the mounting of the leaves on little projections, as described under Spruces.

It is not a large family, not more than two or three species being extensively planted in the United States. The needles are from one-fourth to one-half inch long, arranged in two rows, dark green above, lustrous and slightly bluish beneath. The margin of the leaf is minutely serrulate (like the edge of a saw). The new buds are rather pointed and of a brownish color.

Needles of the Yews

Leaves of the Yew are usually flat and in two rows or ranks along the branchlet. See figure 11. Some European writers maintain that all Yews are of one species, *Taxus baccata,* with many variations. This opinion is held because of the marked similarity of the various species. However, there are at least seven generally-recognized species and numerous horticultural variations. There is no difficulty in distinguishing Yews, as a family, from other genera of Evergreens because of the cup-shaped, berry-like, scarlet fruit.

The identification of the separate species of the Yews is a task requiring close consideration of minute botanical differences. There are so many cultivated forms that it may be safely said that no living person could correctly identify them.

As a family, however, we may say that the leaves are pectinate (like a comb) in arrangement. The upper surface of the leaf is a very dark green, which might be called black-green. Generally they are shiny and leathery in appearance. The underside of the leaves is pale green or yellowish green.

The leaves of the Japanese Yew (*Taxus cuspidata*) average one-half to one and one-half inches long, one-sixteenth to one-twelfth inch wide.

Fig. 11

CHAPTER VIII

Observations on the Rate of Growth in Evergreens

HOW fast a tree grows is a question which seems of great interest to planters, due no doubt to the widespread impression that Evergreens grow very slowly. It is true that most Evergreens are slower growers than other kinds of trees and shrubs. For this same reason they generally live longer.

Slow growth has some advantages. Because of slower growth, trees planted in foundation-plantings or other constricted areas will remain small for many years longer than shrubs.

However, under favorable conditions, many Evergreens really make remarkable progress after they become established. After being transplanted, it takes one or two years for any Evergreen to recover its balance and start to put on normal growth. Results after that depend upon a number of conditions as outlined below.

Consider first the traits of the species; that is, the natural growth tendencies of the particular family.

The peculiar characteristics of an individual tree have a bearing on growth. Trees have individual characters the same as the human race. Occasional specimens make abnormal development; others are unusually retarded.

The soil conditions, whether favorable or unfavorable to the particular kind of tree, influence growth.

Rainfall or moisture conditions are important. In periods of prolonged drought the growth may be only half, or less than half as much as during a rainy season.

Fertilizing influences growth materially. The state of cultivation maintained around the tree is a factor.

The greatest influence on growth is the length of the growing season, which varies, of course, in different localities.

For example, a specimen of a Juniper may make an annual growth of eight inches in northern Illinois, where the growing season starts in late May and stops in October; while the same tree will grow twice as fast in Texas, where the season begins a month or more earlier and continues later in the fall.

In forestry operations, where rapidity of growth is of more vital importance, extensive experiments have been made to determine the influence of the sources of seed on the rapidity of development. It is found that seed from one source will grow trees more than twice as fast as seed from some other source.

Trees in the forest make an entirely different development than individual trees planted separately in an open location. Forest trees, when crowded closely together, make few side branches and shoot straight up to the light with an amazing growth of the main trunk. Therefore, any references to rate of growth, as reported in books on forestry, must be noted with this fact in mind.

These remarks should, therefore, make it easier to understand why no one can accurately say that a certain species of Evergreen will invariably make a certain number of inches of growth per year.

The rate of growth as reported in the following table indicates the growth of the terminal or tip of the tree. The growth of the side branches will be a little less in proportion. Occasionally a freak growth of the terminal bud occurs when there has been an injury to several of the side branches.

In such cases, it is not unusual to see a growth of three feet or more, as the entire energy of the tree goes into the growth of one branch. This condition is more likely to occur in species which start their new growth very early in the season, such as some of the Firs. The side-branch buds may be frozen by late frosts, and the growth is stopped on these branches for the season. When this damage occurs, the long, terminal shoot must be at least partly cut off in order to prevent a big gap in the layers of the branches.

The observations as tabulated below cover a three-year check on the annual growth of a number of Evergreens in northern Illinois. The three-year period includes one year of extreme drought, the summer of 1934, and the season of 1935, a year of great excess rainfall. The figures given for each year include the average growth of at least three separate trees. We wish to again point out that other trees may show quite different results, depending on the many influences discussed above. This list covers only a few representative trees grown in this locality. The trees checked were established specimens, several years old, which had been growing under favorable conditions.

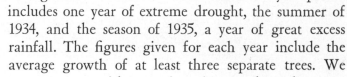

It is not difficult to tell the annual growth of Pines, Firs and Spruces. As shown in this picture, one year's growth includes the tip or terminal growth, and the top whorl or layer of branches. The previous year's growth is the next layer of branches, etc. It takes closer observation to determine the annual growth of Junipers, Arborvitaes, and other Evergreens which do not grow in definite whorls of branches.

Variety	1933	1934	1935	Average of 3 years
Fir (*Abies*)	Growth in Inches			
Cork (*arizonica*)	5	4	6	5
White (*concolor*)	8	4	14	9
Douglas (*Pseudotsuga douglasi*)	15	12	20	16
Fraser (*fraseri*)	7	6	8	7
Juniper (*Juniperus*)				
Column Chinese (*chinensis columnaris*)	12	8	12	11
Pfitzer (*pfitzeriana*)	15	12	18	15
Sargent (*sargenti*)	10	8	12	10
Von Ehron (*sabina von ehron*)	10	8	12	10
Redcedar (*virginiana*)	12	8	15	12
Silver Redcedar (*virginiana glauca*)	8	9	12	9
Cannart Redcedar (*virginiana cannarti*)	7	8	12	9
Spruce (*Picea*)				
White (*canadensis*)	12	8	15	12
Black Hill (*canadensis albertiana*)	8	6	12	9
Norway (*excelsa*)	12	6	20	13
Dwarf Alberta (*glauca conica*)	2	1½	2½	2
Kosters Blue (*pungens kosteriana*)	10	8	15	11
Pine (*Pinus*)				
Mugho (*mughus*)	7	5	8	7
Austrian (*nigra*)	11	7	15	11
Swiss Stone (*cembra*)	6	4	8	6
Scotch (*sylvestris*)	15	10	20	15
Yew (*Taxus*)				
Japanese (*cuspidata*)	10	8	14	11
Dwarf Japanese (*cuspidata nana*)	6	5	8	6
Hicks (*media hicksi*)	12	8	15	12
Arborvitae (*Thuya*)				
American (*occidentalis*)	10	8	12	11
Hemlock (*Tsuga*) American (*canadensis*)	12	9	14	12

CHAPTER IX

New Races of Evergreens for the Future

SCIENTIFIC breeding of animals has been going on for hundreds of years. New strains of horses, cattle, hogs, and even fowls have immeasurably increased the value of these animals for human use. Flowers have been hybridized, and new beauty thus provided for our gardens. The eminent Luther Burbank was rewarded with remarkable accomplishments in the field of fruits and vegetables. His efforts gave to the world plant improvements of inestimable value.

It has remained for the Institute of Forest Genetics at Placerville, Calif., to undertake the first planned effort in developing new Evergreens for forest planting. This institution was founded in 1925 as the Eddy Tree Breeding Station, by John Eddy, whose family has long been associated with the lumber industry.

The main goal of the institution is to develop a race, or several races, of Evergreens that will produce merchantable timber in twenty-five years rather than in the fifty to seventy-five years necessary with existing types of trees. Naturally such an undertaking must be carried on by an institution which will be able to extend its experiments over many years. It will take more than one lifetime to accomplish the results sought for.

Already many valuable observations have been made. First, has been the handpicking of seed from selected trees. Only those trees of the best stature and vitality are chosen. Observations have already established the relation of altitude to tree growth. Hereditary traits are studied through the offspring.

| 800-1900 | 2000-3000 | 3400-3700 | 4100-4700 | 5400-5800 |

ELEVATION IN FEET

ALTITUDE RELATED TO INHERENT VIGOR

A graphic representation of the *average inherent vigor* of groups of mother trees of El Dorado County Western Yellow Pine that are growing at different elevations, based not on their size but on the average growth of their offspring in the Institute's nursery. The hereditary vigor of the low-altitude strain was found to be 71 per cent greater than that of the high-altitude strain. Within each group also occur marked individual variations, and discovery of an inherently superior tree at 3,700 feet points the way to a new strain, both vigorous and hardy.

The delicate process of making a cross by hybridizing the promising trees has already begun. In one year 8,000 flowers of conifers were pollinated by hand. Forty-four species are already planted in the arboretum. It is the hope that the best characteristics of different species may be combined to produce a tree of superior value for reforestation.

We have been guilty, as everyone knows, of almost criminal negligence in replacing our forests. Over fifteen acres of pulp-wood are required for one Sunday edition of a large city newspaper. Our forests are denuded of nearly 20,000 square miles each year. It therefore becomes of the most vital importance, if, by any possible human effort, the necessary time to replace the forests can be reduced by one-half or more.

The remarkable advantage of developing quicker-growing forests is clearly shown in the following statistics taken from a pamphlet published by the Institute of Forest Genetics, Placerville, California.

A GREAT SAVING TO THE GROWER

Professor Walter Mulford, head of the Division of Forestry of the University of California, estimates that it will cost only about thirty percent as much to grow a crop of "twenty-five-year" trees as it does to grow a crop of "fifty-year" trees, initial costs being equal. Indeed, the figures show that to cut ten years off the growing time, at any stage, will reduce the growing cost approximately forty percent. This is arrived at by a calculation of compound interest charges on the original investment, without taking into consideration the cost of fire prevention and upkeep, ordinarily offset by the value of posts, poles, and firewood obtained from thinnings.

Moreover, the land will produce two crops and two profits in fifty years instead of only one.

FAST- AND SLOW-GROWING PINES

In the foreground are two-year-old Sugar Pine seedlings only a few inches high; in the background, Monterey Pines *of the same age!* Monterey Pine is the fastest-growing species found to date, and a hybrid form may be of great value. The tallest seedling is 4.37 feet high.

This picture and the one on the opposite page furnished through the courtesy of Institute of Forest Genetics, Placerville, California

CHAPTER X

Dwarf Evergreens

UNDER the heading of Dwarf Evergreens are (1) the natural dwarfs, the Tom Thumb trees from normal size parents, (2) the varieties grown from "witches brooms," (3) the climatic dwarfs, and (4) the artificial dwarfs.

The Japanese are especially adept at dwarfing trees by artificial means. Anyone can "dwarf" a tree by the simple process of early and frequent pruning. These trees, of course, do not produce dwarf offspring, and, therefore, are not truly dwarf trees, in the sense of bearing new names or of being considered as new varieties.

The climatic dwarfs result from some adverse growing condition. Many varieties which make an upright, tree-like growth at low altitudes develop into mere shrubs or creepers when they encroach upon the higher mountain sides. Some of these trees reproduce the dwarf habit of their parents. About twenty years ago, the late Prof. C. S. Sargent, who was for 50 years the guiding hand of the famous Arnold Arboretum, observed some Red Cedars which had been growing on a wind-swept cliff on the coast of Maine. These trees, which normally were of upright habit, had been reduced to low-spreading bushes by the constant severe winds blowing against them. He sent wood for grafting to

This is an example of a "Witches Broom" growing on a Norway Spruce in southern Wisconsin. Photograph courtesy Mr. Virgil Bevan. From such curious deformities many dwarf evergreens have been produced.

38

Mr. D. Hill, who grafted several trees to observe what the behavior of the trees would be. A few of these specimens remaining at the Hill Nursery continue to take the dwarf form of the parent trees.

"Witches Brooms" is the name given to the curious, nest-like deformities found at times on otherwise normal trees. They are a dense, thick growth of small twigs and branches thought to be formed by insect irritations. When grafts are taken from these growths, an extremely dwarf tree will frequently result. Many of the dwarf types of Evergreens in the trade, particularly dwarf Spruce, were developed from these curious freaks.

The natural dwarfs are those oddities which develop by the same prank of nature that produces the Tom Thumbs of the human race. Many such dwarfs have been found either in a wild state or in cultivated grounds. Among the best known trees of this origin is the Dwarf Alberta Spruce. This dwarf, cone-shaped Spruce was found 30 years ago by Prof. Jack of the Arnold Arboretum staff at Lake Laggan, in the Canadian Rockies.

Dwarf conifers are, of course, of little importance. Nevertheless, they are an interesting study. When Louden wrote of Evergreens in 1838, he mentioned only ten dwarf forms. A few years later the Frenchman, Carriere, in 1865, records forty. The German writer, Beissner, about 35 years later, listed more than 150. Murray Hornibrook, reporting to the Conifer Conference in London in 1932, says he has found 500. Such an assortment is, of course, beyond the realm of any practical use, but it well illustrates the infinite complexities of nature.

Some dwarf Evergreens result from environment. Seed from wind swept Pines such as these would likely produce dwarf trees even though the parent trees were originally of an upright, tall growing species.

Chapter XI

Evergreen Families of the World

JUST how to define the trees popularly called "Evergreens" is somewhat of a problem. If we say that they are trees which keep their leaves in winter, we find that this definition is not adequate because there are other trees, not Evergreens, which also keep their leaves in winter. In fact, almost all trees in warmer climates keep their leaves throughout the year. Strangely, we also have some families of Evergreens which shed their leaves in winter: the Larches and the Bald Cypress. There are, of course, botanical differences, such as the resinous sap, and the nature of the flowers and seed, which may help to define Evergreens.

The tangled mass of tree life which exists throughout the world, we may conveniently think of as falling into orderly man-made divisions: the order, the family, and the tribe. It is true that upon this structure our system of plant classification is based. Without it, the science of botany would slip back into the confusion from which eminent scientists have so long struggled to sift and sort the intricate ramifications of plant life.

However, Evergreens which defy being laid to rest in their proper niche in the great system are forever bobbing up. Even today there is often a difference of opinion as to whether a tree belongs here or there. After all, trees are like people. They are individuals; no two are exactly alike. We find individual characteristics without number. For example, probably one hundred forms of American Arborvitae have been propagated within the last three hundred years.

Many new varieties have been given life by nurserymen. One has but to consult the nursery catalogs of a few generations ago, to realize the great mortality which overtakes many varieties. The tree they represented has long since disappeared for one reason or another. New varieties lacking any special merit soon lose favor with the public and are lost sight of forever. Sometimes they again appear, dressed up with a new name.

Thus, we may view horticultural varieties as constantly changing, as the fickle hand of nature adds a different characteristic to some tree.

System of Classification

We must have at least some understanding of the system of classification of Evergreens in order to view the subject intelligently. This system can be easily learned by any one who has no botanical knowledge whatever. We may compare Evergreens to the human races of the world, which are again divided into nationalities, which might be further divided into groups, according to stature or facial characteristics. For example, in the Caucasian or white race, we have the French, the Germans, the English, etc. If the comparison to the botanical system were continued, we would divide the English nationality into many varieties, separating people according to the color of their eyes, their height, girth, etc.

The first division of Evergreens is the *Genus*. For example, Pine, Spruce, Fir, etc. Each genus is then divided into its species, and in turn under each species we list the individual varieties. For example:

Genus: Juniperus (Juniper)
Species: Juniperus chinensis (Chinese Juniper)
Variety: Juniperus chinensis pfitzeriana (Pfitzer Juniper)

Of the first great division there are generally recognized forty-two genera (Genus) of Evergreens known in the world. The number of genera is quite firmly fixed as almost all great Evergreen families of the world have now been discovered and either given a genus name of their own or are included in some other genus. However, some additional changes may be made in time to come.

Not All Genera in Cultivation

Of these forty-two families, we may pass over eighteen as being of little interest to us. Many of these are from tropical climates and are not hardy in most sections of the United States, or they are not of sufficient interest to be chosen for cultivated use. The names of the eighteen genera referred to are as follows:

Genus	*Where Found*	*Genus*	*Where Found*
Acmopyle	Pacific Islands	Glyptostrobus	China
Actinostrobus	Western Australia	Keteleeria	China—Japan
Agathis	New Zealand	Microcachrys	Tasmania
Amentotaxus	China—Japan	Pherosphaera	Tasmania
Athrotaxis	Tasmania	Phyllocladus	Philippine Islands
Austrotaxus	Loyalty Islands	Saxegothaea	Chile
Callitris	The Southern Hemisphere	Taiwani	Formosa
		Tetraclinis	Spain—Africa
Dacrydium	Australia—Chile	Widdringtonia	Africa
Fitzroya	Chile		

This leaves a remainder of twenty-four genera to which practically all Evergreens commonly planted in the United States belong. A list of these twenty-four genera will be found in the following pages, together with their different species and varieties.

This list is made up from standard sources of reference, representing the trees thought to be in cultivation in the United States.

However, as it is our desire to present readers with practical information and to simplify, rather than to add to, the confusion that confronts a student of Evergreens, we have checked this list against the catalogs of leading nurserymen to find which trees actually are offered for sale at the present time.

One hundred thirty-four catalogs were checked, representing the leading nursery establishments of the country, located from Maine to California, and from Minnesota to Florida. None of the eighteen genera previously mentioned were found. Of the two hundred fifty species contained in the list, about one half, or one hundred thirty, were not offered in any catalog. In the list of about five hundred varieties, nearly three hundred seventy were found, leaving one hundred thirty varieties not known to be in any nursery. It is not surprising at the same time to find approximately eighty horticultural varieties listed in the catalogs, which are not contained in the following pages.

This fact accounts for the small attention that scientific writers give to varieties, which are continually springing up. At the same time, many horticultural varieties are among the most important ornamental Evergreens.

To summarize this investigation, we find:

Number of genera listed in catalogs checked 24
Number of species listed in catalogs checked 130
Number of varieties listed in catalogs checked 370

Total number of species and varieties 500

We do not mean to infer that other species and varieties of Evergreens do not exist within the United States, because it is doubtless true that many smaller local nurseries have other trees; and it is also true that many collections of Evergreens in arboretums and elsewhere contain a much greater assortment. The fact remains, however, that approximately five hundred species and varieties cover the assortment available to planters from the principal nurseries in this country.

To further simplify our conception of the Evergreen family, we can safely say that out of the twenty-four genera of Evergreens mentioned, the greater part of plantings is made up of not over twelve of these families.

In the vicinity of Chicago the list is still further reduced, the great majority of plantings consist of Firs, Junipers, Spruces, Pines, Arborvitaes, Yews, and Hemlocks. In each section of the country different genera predominate, depending upon climatic conditions. Elsewhere in this book descriptions and illustrations are given of many of the most widely-used Evergreens.

FIR (Abies)

Abies alba (Silver Fir)
    (Also called Abies pectinata)
Abies amabilis (Cascade Fir)
Abies arizonica (Cork Fir)
    var. compacta
Abies balsamea (Balsam Fir)
    var. hudsonia (Hudson Fir)
    var. macrocarpa
Abies borisii regis (King Boris Fir)
Abies brachyphylla
    (Also known as Abies homolepis)
Abies cephalonica (Greek Fir)
    var. apollonis (Apollo Fir)
Abies chensiensis (Shensi Fir)
Abies cilicica (Cilician Fir)
Abies concolor (White Fir)
    var. argentea
    var. aurea
    var. brevifolia
    var. conica
    var. globosa
    var. violacea (Purplecone White Fir)
    var. wattezii
Abies concolor lowiana (Pacific White Fir)
Abies delavayi (Delavay Fir)
Abies fargesii (Farges Fir)

Abies faxoniana (Faxon Fir)
Abies firma (Momi Fir)
Abies fraseri (Fraser Fir)
    var. compacta
    var. prostrata
Abies grandis (Great Silver Fir)
Abies holophylla (Needle Fir)
Abies homolepis (Nikko Fir)
    var. scottae (Dwarf Nikko Fir)
    var. tomomi
    var. umbellata (Dimplecone Fir)
Abies insignis (Hybrid of A. nordmanniana
    and A. pinsapo)
Abies koreana (Korean Fir)
Abies lasiocarpa (Alpine Fir)
Abies magnifica (Red Fir)
    var. argentea
    var. glauca (Azure Fir)
    var. shastensis (Shasta Fir)
Abies mariesii (Maries Fir)
Abies nobilis (Noble Fir)
    var. argentea
    var. glauca (Blueleaf Noble Fir)
Abies nordmanniana (Nordmann Fir)
    var. aurea
    var. tortifolia
Abies numidica (Algerian Fir)

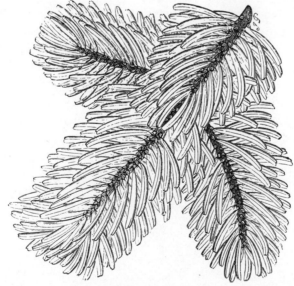

Foliage of the Fir

FIR (Abies)—continued

Abies pectinata (Silver Fir)
    var. pendula (Weeping Silver Fir)
    var. pyramidalis (Sentinel Silver Fir)
    var. pumila
Abies pindrow (Pindrow Fir)
Abies pinsapo (Spanish Fir)
    var. argentea
    var. glauca (Blue Spanish Fir)
    var. pendula (Weeping Spanish Fir)
Abies recurvata (Min Fir)
Abies religiosa (Sacred Fir)
Abies sachalinensis (Sakhalin Fir)
    var. nemorensis
Abies sibirica (Siberian Fir)
Abies spectabilis (Himalayan Fir)
Abies squamata (Flaky Fir)

Abies veitchii (Veitch Fir)
Abies venusta (Bristlecone Fir)

About 15 additional varieties of dwarf firs are mentioned in "Dwarf and Slow Growing Conifers"—Hornibrook.

ARAUCARIA (Araucaria)

Araucaria bidwilli (Bunya-Bunya)
Araucaria brasiliana (Brazilian Araucaria)
    (Also known as A. angustifolia)
Araucaria excelsa (Norfolk Island Pine)
Araucaria imbricata (Monkey Puzzle)
    (Also known as A. araucana)

(Note: At least 3 other species are known, but little used, as well as several horticultural varieties, particularly of A. excelsa)

Foliage of Araucaria

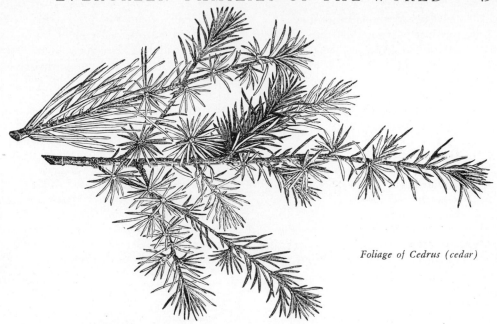

Foliage of Cedrus (cedar)

CEDRUS (Cedar)

Cedrus atlantica (Atlas Cedar)
    var. argentea (Silver Atlas Cedar)
    var. aurea (Golden Atlas Cedar)
    var. fastigiata (Sentinel Cedar)
    var. glauca (Blue Atlas Cedar)
    var. pendula (Drooping Atlas Cedar)
Cedrus deodara (Deodar Cedar)
    var. argentea (Silver Deodar Cedar)
    var. aurea (Golden Deodar Cedar)
    var. crassifolia
    var. pendula (Drooping Deodar Cedar)
    var. robusta (Longleaf Deodar Cedar)
    var. verticillata (Hardy Deodar Cedar)
    var. viridis (Green Deodar Cedar)
Cedrus libani (Cedar of Lebanon)
    (Also has yellow, blue and weeping forms)

CEPHALOTAXUS (Plum Yew)

Cephalotaxus drupacea (Japanese Plum Yew)
    var. fastigiata (Spiral Plum Yew)
Cephalotaxus fortuni (Chinese Plum Yew)
Cephalotaxus harringtonia (pedunculata) (Harrington Plum Yew)
    (Note: There is at least one other species and two or three little known additional varieties of cephalotaxus.)

CHAMAECYPARIS (False Cypress)

Chamaecyparis lawsoniana (Lawson Cypress)
    var. albospica (Cream Cypress)
    var. allumi (Scarab Cypress)
    var. argentea (Silver Lawson Cypress)
    var. bowleri

Foliage of Cephalotaxus (Plum Yew)

Chamaecyparis lawsoniana—*continued*

    var. erecta viridis (Green Column Cypress)

    var. erecta glauca

    var. filiformis

    var. fraseri

    var. glauca (Steel Cypress)

    var. gracilis (Fountain Lawson Cypress)

    var. krameri

    var. lutea (Golden Lawson Cypress)

    var. nana (Dwarf Lawson Cypress)

    var. nana glauca

    var. nidiformis

    var. pendula (Weeping Lawson Cypress)

    var. pyramidalis alba (White Sentry Cypress)

    var. stewarti

    var. Triomphe de Boskoop

    var. versicolor

    var. westermanni (Westermann Cypress)

    var. wisseli (Wissel Cypress)

    var. youngi (Young Cypress)

The above are the best known varieties. At least 25 additional varieties have been named. The Lawson Cypress is one of the most variable species.

Chamaecyparis nootkatensis (Nootka Cypress)

    var. compacta

    var. glauca (Blue Nootka Cypress)

    var. lutea

    var. pendula

Chamaecyparis obtusa (Hinoki Cypress)

    var. formosana

    var. albo-spicata

    var. aurea (Golden Hinoki Cypress)

    var. compacta (Football Cypress)

    var. crippsi (Cripps Golden Cypress)

    var. erecta

    var. ericoides (Sander Retinospora)

    var. filicoides (Fernspray Retinospora)

    var. gracilis aurea (Yellow-tip Hinoki Cypress)

    var. lycopodioides (Clubmoss Retinospora)

    var. magnifica

Chamaecyparis obtusa—*continued*

    var. nana (Dwarf Hinoki Cypress)

    var. pendula (Weeping Hinoki Cypress)

    var. pygmaea (Pygmy Hinoki Cypress)

There are many additional forms.

Chamaecyparis thyoides (White Cedar)

    var. andelyensis (Andely Retinospora)

    var. ericoides (Cedar Retinospora)

    var. glauca (Blue White Cedar)

    var. hoveyi

    var. variegata (Variegated White Cedar)

Chamaecyparis pisifera (Sawara Cypress)

    var. aurea (Golden Sawara Cypress)

    var. filifera (Thread Retinospora)

    var. filifera aurea (Golden Thread Retinospora)

    var. filifera nana (Dwarf Thread Retinospora)

    var. plumosa (Plume Retinospora)

    var. plumosà argentea (Silver-tip Retinospora)

    var. plumosa aurea (Golden Plume Retinospora)

    var. plumosa lutescens

    var. squarrosa (Moss Retinospora)

    var. squarrosa dumosa

    var. squarrosa sulphurea

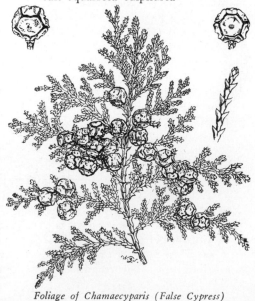

Foliage of Chamaecyparis (False Cypress)

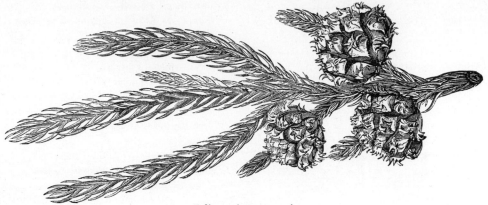

Foliage of Cryptomeria

CRYPTOMERIA (Cryptomeria)

Cryptomeria japonica (Common
    Cryptomeria)
    var. araucarioides
    var. compacta (Cave Cryptomeria)
    var. cristata
    var. elegans (Plume Cryptomeria)
    var. elegans gracilis (Slender
      Cryptomeria)

    var. lobbi (Lobb Cryptomeria)
    var. nana
    var. pungens (Prickly Cryptomeria)
    var. selaginoides
    var. spiralis

CUNNINGHAMIA (China Fir)

Cunninghamia lanceolata (China Fir)
Cunninghamia konishi (Formosa Fir)

Foliage of Cunninghamia (China Fir)

Foliage of Cupressus (Cypress)

CUPRESSUS (Cypress)

Cupressus arizonica (Arizona Cypress)
Cupressus compacta
Cupressus glauca
Cupressus benthami (Bentham Cypress)
    var. knightiana (Knight Cypress)
  (The above two may be varieties of C.
lusitanica)
Cupressus funebris (Mourning Cypress)
Cupressus glabra (Smooth Cypress)
    (Also known as C. arizonica bonita)
Cupressus goveniana (Gowen Cypress)
    var. glauca (Blue Gowen Cypress)
Cupressus guadalupensis (Guadalupe
    Cypress)
    var. glauca (Blue Guadalupe Cypress)
Cupressus lusitanica (Portuguese Cypress)
Cupressus macnabiana (Macnab Cypress)
    var. sulphurea (Yellow Macnab
    Cypress)
Cupressus macrocarpa (Monterey Cypress)
    var. crippsii (Cripps Cypress)
    var. fastigiata

Cupressus macrocarpa—*continued*
    var. lutea (Yellow Monterey Cypress)
    var. variegata
Cupressus sempervirens (Italian Cypress)
    var. stricta (fastigiata) (Columnar
    Italian Cypress)
    var. indica (Globe-cone Italian
    Cypress)
    var. horizontalis (Spreading Italian
    Cypress)
Cupressus torulosa (Bhutan Cypress)
    var. corneyana (Corney Cypress)
    var. majestica (Lofty Cypress)

JUNIPERUS (Juniper)

Juniperus ashei (Ozark White Cedar)
Juniperus barbadensis (J. bermudiana)
    (Bermuda Juniper)
Juniperus californica (California Juniper)
Juniperus chinensis (Chinese Juniper)
    var. albo-variegata (Whiteleaf Chinese
    Juniper)
    var. aurea (Golden Chinese Juniper)
    var. aureo-globosa
    var. femina (Reeves Juniper)
    var. fortunei (Also known as J.
    sphaerica
    var. globosa (Globe Chinese Juniper)
    var. japonica (J. *japonica*)
    var. mas
    var. neaboriensis (Also known as J.
    macrocarpa)
    var. oblonga
    var. pendula (Weeping Chinese
    Juniper)
    var. pfitzeriana (Pfitzer Juniper)
    var. pfitzeriana aurea (Hill Golden
    Pfitzer Juniper)
    var. plumosa
    var. plumosa aurea
    var. pyramidalis (J. columnaris)
    (Column Chinese Juniper)
    (Both blue and green forms)
    var. sargenti (Sargent Juniper)
    (Both blue and green forms)
    var. sheppardi
    var. smithi
    var. torulosa

Juniperus communis (Common Juniper)
 var. depressa (J. canadensis) (Prostrate Juniper)
 var. depressa ashfordi (Ashford Juniper)
 var. depressa aurea (Golden Prostrate Juniper)
 var. depressa plumosa (Andorra Juniper)
 (Also known as J. horizontalis plumosa)
 var. depressa vase shaped
 var. cracovia (Polish Juniper)
 var. echinoformis (Hedgehog Juniper)
 var. grayii—Plant patent no. 54
 var. hibernica (Irish Juniper)
 var. jacki
 var. montana (Mountain Juniper)
 var. oblonga-pendula (Weeping Juniper)
 var. suecica (Swedish Juniper)
 var. suecica nana (Dwarf Swedish Juniper)
 (A few other varieties of J. communis are named.)
Juniperus cedrus (Canary Island Juniper)
Juniperus conferta (Shore Juniper)
Juniperus drupacea (Syrian Juniper)
Juniperus excelsa (Greek Juniper)
 var. stricta (Spiny Greek Juniper)
 var. variegata (Variegated Greek Juniper)
Juniperus formosana (Formosa Juniper)
Juniperus horizontalis (Creeping Juniper)
 var. douglasii (Waukegan Juniper)
 var. alpina
 var. glomerata
 var. variegata
 var. plumosa (Andorra Juniper)
 (Also known as J. communis depressa plumosa)
 var. procumbens
 (Some of the above have been known as varieties of J. sabina.)
Juniperus japonica (Japanese Juniper)
 (Trees under this name are considered by some authorities as varieties of Juniperus chinensis.)

Juniperus japonica—*continued*
 var. aurea (Golden Japanese Juniper)
 var. aureovariegata (Variegated Dwarf Japanese Juniper)
 var. nana (Hill Japanese Juniper)
 var. sylvestris
Juniperus lucayana (West Indian Redcedar) (Southern Redcedar)
 var. bedfordiana
Juniperus macrocarpa (Plum Juniper) (known as J. chinensis neaboriensis)
Juniperus monosperma (Cherrystone Juniper)
Juniperus morrisonicola (Mt. Morrison Juniper)
Juniperus occidentalis (Western Juniper)
Juniperus oxycedrus (Prickly Juniper)
Juniperus pachyphlaea (Alligator Juniper)
Juniperus phoenicea (Phoenicean Juniper)
Juniperus procera (African Juniper)
Juniperus recurva (Drooping Juniper)
Juniperus rigida (Needle Juniper)
Juniperus sabina (Savin Juniper)
 var. cupressifolia (Cypress Savin Juniper)
 var. fastigiata (Column Savin Juniper)
 var. horizontalis (Bar Harbor Juniper)
 var. lusitanica
 var. prostrata hilli
 var. pyramidalis (Pyramidal Savin Juniper)
 var. tamariscifolia (Tamarix Savin Juniper)
 var. variegata (Hoarfrost Savin Juniper)
 var. von ehron (Von Ehron Juniper)
Juniperus scopulorum (Colorado Juniper)
 var. Marshall Juniper
 var. Chandler Juniper
 The Juniperus scopulorum has been a specialty of the D. Hill Nursery Company. The following are named varieties.
 var. Blue Moon Juniper
 var. Hill Silver Juniper
 var. Moonlight Juniper
 var. North Star Juniper
 var. Silver Queen Juniper
 var. Victory Juniper

Juniperus squamata (Himalayan Juniper)
    var. albovariegata
    var. fargesi
    var. meyeri (Meyer Juniper)
    var. wilsoni
Juniperus thurifera (Spanish Juniper)
Juniperus utahensis (Utah Juniper)
    var. megalocarpa
Juniperus virginiana (Redcedar)
    var. albo-spica (White-tip Redcedar)
    var. aurea
    var. burki (Burk Juniper)
    var. cannarti (Cannart Redcedar)
    var. chamberlaynii (Chamberlayn Red-
       cedar)
    var. cylindrica (Column Redcedar)
    var. elegantissima (Goldtip Redcedar)
    var. filifera

Juniperus virginiana—*continued*
    var. glauca (Silver Redcedar)
    var. globosa (Globe Redcedar)
    var. keteleeri (Keteleer Redcedar)
    var. kosteri (Koster Redcedar)
    var. pendula (Weeping Redcedar)
    var. pyramidalis viridis
    var. pyramidalis hilli (Hill Pyramidal
       Juniper)
    var. pyramidiformia hilli (Hill Dundee
       Juniper)
    var. reptans (Creeping Redcedar)
    var. schotti (Schott Redcedar)
    var. smithi (Smith Redcedar)
    var. tripartita (Fountain Redcedar)
    var. triomphe D'Angiers
    var. venusta
Juniperus wallichiana (Black Juniper)

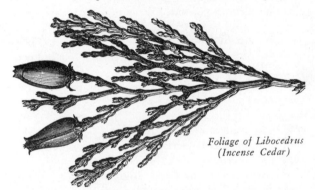

Foliage of Libocedrus
(Incense Cedar)

Foliage of Larix (Larch)

LARIX (Larch)

Larix dahurica (gmelini) (Dahurian Larch)
    var. japonica
    var. principis rupprechti (Prince Rupprecht Larch)
Larix eurolepis (Dunkeld Larch)
Larix europea (decidua) (European Larch)
    var. pendula (Weeping European Larch)
    var. pyramidalis (Pyramidal European Larch)
Larix laricini (American Larch) (Tamarack)
Larix occidentalis (Western Larch)
Larix potaninii (China Larch)
Larix sibirica (Siberian Larch)

LIBOCEDRUS

Libocedrus decurrens (Incense Cedar)
    var. compacta
Libocedrus chilensis (Chilean Incense Cedar)

(There are several other species and some
varieties are known which are but little cultivated.)

PICEA (Spruce)

Picea abies
  (This name is used by Bailey to desig-
  nate the tree commonly known as
  Picea excelsa [Norway Spruce].)
Picea alcockiana (Alcock Spruce)
  (Sometimes known as Picea Bicolor)
  var. acicularis
  var. reflexa
Picea albertiana (Alberta Spruce)
  (A British Columbia species not known
  in the trade)
Picea breweriana (Brewer Spruce)
Picea canadensis (White Spruce)
  (The name Picea glauca is used by
  Bailey)
  var. aurea (Golden White Spruce)
  var. caerulea (Silver White Spruce)
  var. (glauca) conica (Dwarf Alberta
  Spruce)
  var. tabuliformis
Picea canadensis albertiana (Black Hill
  Spruce)
  (This tree is designated by Bailey as
  Picea glauca densata)
Picea complanata
Picea engelmanni (Engelmann Spruce)
  var. argentea
  var. fendleri
  var. glauca (Blue Engelmann Spruce)
Picea excelsa (Norway Spruce) (Picea abies)
  (The horticultural variations of Norway
  Spruce run into hundreds. Following are important varieties:)
  var. argentea
  var. argenteo-spicata (Silver Norway
  Spruce)
  var. aurea (Golden Norway Spruce)
  var. aurescens
  var. barryi (Barry Spruce)
  var. capitata
  var. chlorocarpa
  var. cincinnata
  var. clanbrasiliana (Clanbrasil Spruce)
  (Standardized Plant Names indicates
  synonymous with P. barryi)
  var. columnaris
  var. compacta (Globe Norway Spruce)

Picea excelsa—*continued*
  var. conica (Arrowhead Norway
  Spruce)
  var. cranstoni (Cranston Norway
  Spruce)
  var. cupressina
  var. diffusa
  var. dumosa
  var. echinae formis
  var. elegans (Knight Norway Spruce)
  var. ellwangeriana (Ellwanger Spruce)
  var. erythrocarpa
  var. finedonensis (Finedon Spruce)
  var. gregoryana (Gregory Spruce)
  var. highlandia
  var. humilis
  var. inversa
  var. maxwelli (Maxwell Spruce)
  var. merki (Merk Spruce)
  var. microsperma
  var. monstrosa
  var. mucronata
  var. nana
  var. nidiformis (Nest-shaped Spruce)
  var. nigra
  var. ohlendorffi
  var. parsoni
  var. parviformis (Dwarf Pyramid
  Spruce)
  var. pendula (Weeping Norway
  Spruce)
  var. procumbens (Prostrate Norway
  Spruce)
  var. pseudo-maxwelli
  var. pumila
  var. pumila nigra
  var. pygmaea (Pygmy Spruce)
  var. pyramidata (pyramidalis) (Pyramidal Norway Spruce)
  var. remonti (Remont Spruce)
  var. repens
  var. robusta (Burly Norway Spruce)
  var. smithi (Smith Norway Spruce)
  var. tabuliformis
  var. viminalis
  var. virgata
There are many additional forms.

Picea glehni (Saghalin Spruce) (Sakhalin)
Picea jezoensis (Yeddo Spruce) (Yezo)
    var. hondoensis (Hondo Spruce)
Picea mariana (Black Spruce)
    var. doumeti (Doumet Spruce)
    var. ericoides
    var. fastigiata
Picea maximowiczi (Japanese Bush Spruce)
Picea meyeri (Meyer Chinese Spruce)
Picea obovata (Siberian Spruce)
    var. alpestris
    var. fennica
Picea omorika (Serbian Spruce)
    var. pendula
Picea orientalis (Oriental Spruce)
    var. aurea
    var. aureo-spicata
    var. nana
Picea polita (Tigertail Spruce)
Picea pungens (Colorado Spruce)
    var. argentea (Silver Blue Spruce)
    var. aurea (Golden Blue Spruce)
    var. bakeri (Baker Blue Spruce)

Picea pungens—continued
    var. caerulea
    var. compacta (Dwarf Colorado Blue Spruce)
    var. glauca (Colorado Blue Spruce)
    var. hoopsi (Hoops Blue Spruce)
    var. kosteriana (Koster Blue Spruce)
    var. moerheimi (Moerheim Blue Spruce)
    var. pendula (Weeping Blue Spruce)
    var. viridis (Green Colorado Spruce)
Picea rubra (Red Spruce) (P. rubens)
    var. virgata
    var. monstrosa
Picea sargentiana (Sargent Chinese Spruce)
Picea schrenkiana (Asian Spruce)
Picea sitchensis (Sitka Spruce)
    var. speciosa
Picea smithiana (Himalayan Spruce)
Picea spinulosa (Sikkim Spruce)

In addition to the above there are several species of Asiatic Spruces introduced by Ernest Wilson, at present little in cultivation.

PINUS (Pine)

Pinus albicaulis (Whitebark Pine)
Pinus aristata (Bristlecone Pine)
Pinus arizonica (Arizona Pine)
    (Also listed as a variety of Pinus Ponderosa)
Pinus armandi (Armand Pine) (Chinese White Pine)
Pinus attenuata (Knobcone Pine)
Pinus ayacahuite (Mexican White Pine)
Pinus balfouriana (Fox Tail Pine)
Pinus banksiana (Jack Pine)
Pinus bungeana (Lacebark Pine)
Pinus canariensis (Canary Pine)
Pinus caribaea (Slash Pine)
Pinus cembra (Swiss Stone Pine)
    var. pumila
    var. sibirica
    var. aurea
    var. columnaris
Pinus cembroides (Mexican Stone Pine)
Pinus clausa (Sand Pine)
Pinus contorta (Shore Pine)

Pinus contorta—continued
    var. latifolia (Lodge Pole Pine)
    (Also known as Pinus murrayana)
Pinus coulteri (Coulter Pine) (Bigcone Pine)
Pinus densiflora (Japanese Red Pine)
    var. albo-terminata (Whitetip Japanese Pine)
    var. aurea (Golden Japanese Pine)
    var. globosa (Globe Japanese Pine)
    var. oculus-draconis (Dragon-eye Pine)
    var. pendula (Weeping Japanese Pine)
    var. umbraculifera (Japanese Umbrella Pine)
    (Sometimes called Pinus tanyosho) (Japanese Table Pine)
Pinus echinata (Shortleaf Pine)
Pinus edulis (Nut Pine) (Pinyon)
    var. albovariegata (Variegated Nut Pine)
Pinus excelsa (Himalayan White Pine)
    (Also known as Pinus nepalensis)
    var. zebrina

Pinus flexilis (Limber Pine)
    var. reflexa
Pinus glabra (Spruce Pine)
Pinus halepensis (Aleppo Pine)
    var. brutia
Pinus insularis (Benguet Pine)
Pinus jeffreyi (Jeffrey Pine)
Pinus koraiensis (Korean Pine)
Pinus lambertiana (Sugar Pine)
Pinus leucodermis (Graybark Pine)
Pinus massoniana
Pinus monophylla (Singleleaf Pine)
Pinus monticola (Western Yellow Pine)
Pinus montana (See below)
Pinus mugo (mugho) (This name is suggested by Bailey to cover the group of Pines of the P. montana family. Thus the following are designated as varieties:)
    var. compacta (Hill Mugho Pine)
    var. mughus (Dwarf Mugho Pine)
    var. pumilio (Bush Pine)
    var. rotundata
    var. slavini
    var. uncinata
Pinus muricata (Bishop Pine)
Pinus murrayana (Lodgepole Pine)
    (Also known as P. contorta—var. latifolia)
Pinus nepalensis
    (Also known as Pinus excelsa)
Pinus nigra (Austrian Pine)
    (Also known as Pinus laricio)
    var. calabrica (poiretiana) (Corsican Pine)
    var. caramanica (Crimean Pine)
    var. cebennensis (Cevennes Pine)
    var. globosa
    var. monstrosa
    var. pendula
    var. prostrata
    var. pygmaea
    var. pyramidalis
Pinus palustris (Longleaf Pine) (Cluster Pine)
    var. hamiltonii (Lord Aberdeen Pine)
Pinus parryana (Parry Pine)
    (Also known as Pinus quadrifolia)

Pinus parviflora (Japanese White Pine)
    var. glauca
    var. nana
Pinus peuke (Macedonian White Pine)
Pinus pinea (Italian Stone Pine)
Pinus ponderosa (Western Yellow Pine)
    var. arizonica
    (Also known as a distinct species—P. arizonica)
    var. scopulorum (Rocky Mountain Yellow Pine)
    var. pendula (Weeping Yellow Pine)
    (There are some additional little known Mexican species)
Pinus pungens (Table Mountain Pine)
Pinus quadrifolia
    (Also known as Pinus parryana)
Pinus radiata (Monterey Pine)
    var. binata
Pinus resinosa (Red or Norway Pine)
    var. globosa
Pinus rigida (Pitch Pine)
Pinus roxburghi (Chir Pine)
Pinus sabiniana (Digger Pine)
Pinus serotina (Pond Pine)
Pinus sinensis
    (Correctly known as P. tabulaeformis)
Pinus strobus (White Pine)
    var. aurea (Golden White Pine)
    var. contorta
    var. fastigiata (Pyramidal White Pine)
    var. glauca (Blue White Pine)
    var. nana (Dwarf White Pine)
    var. nivea
    var. umbraculifera (Umbrella White Pine)
Pinus sylvestris (Scotch Pine)
    var. aurea (Golden Scotch Pine)
    var. argentea
    var. fastigiata
    var. nana
    var. pendula
    var. pumila
    var. rigensis (Riga Pine)
    (A geographical variation)
    var. watereri (Waterer Pine)
There are some other less known varieties.

Pinus tabulaeformis (Chinese Pine)
   var. densata
   var. yunnanensis (Yunnan Pine)
Pinus taeda (Loblolly Pine)
Pinus taiwanensis (Formosa Pine)
Pinus thunbergi (Japanese Black Pine)
Pinus torreyana (Torrey Pine)
Pinus virginiana (Jersey Pine)

TAXODIUM

Taxodium ascendens (Pond Cypress)
   var. pendulum (nutans) (Weeping
      Pond Cypress)
Taxodium distichum (Common Bald Cy-
      press)
   var. fastigiatum
   var. nanum
   var. pendulum
   var. pyramidalis
Taxodium mucronatum (Montezuma Yew-
      Cypress)

PSEUDOTSUGA

Pseudotsuga douglasi (Douglas Fir) (Pacific
      Coast Type)
Pseudotsuga douglasi glauca (Douglas Fir)
      (Rocky Mountain Type)
   (The Rocky Mountain variety is generally
designated simply as Pseudotsuga douglasi)
   var. argentea (Silver Douglas Fir)
   var. brevibracteata
   var. compacta

Pseudotsuga douglasi glauca—*continued*
   var. densa
   var. fastigiata (Pyramidal Douglas Fir)
   var. fretsi (Frets Fir)
   var. glauca pendula (Weeping Doug-
      las Fir)
   var. globosa
   var. pyramidata
   var. viridis
Pseudotsuga macrocarpa (Bigcone Spruce)
Pseudotsuga japonica

PSEUDOLARIX (Golden Larch)

Pseudolarix amabilis

PODOCARPUS

Podocarpus acutifolia
Podocarpus alpina
Podocarpus andina
Podocarpus dacrydioides
Podocarpus elongata
Podocarpus ferruginea
Podocarpus gracilior
Podocarpus halli
Podocarpus macrophylla
Podocarpus nagi
Podocarpus neriifolia
Podocarpus nivalis
Podocarpus nubigena
Podocarpus saligna
Podocarpus spicata
Podocarpus spinulosa
Podocarpus totara

Foliage of Podocarpus

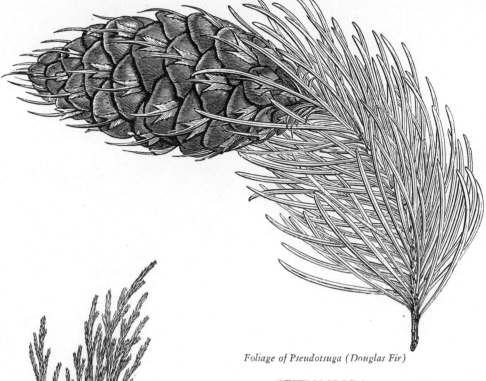

Foliage of Pseudotsuga (Douglas Fir)

RETINOSPORA

Trees formerly called Retinospora are listed as Chamaecyparis, Cupressus or Thuya.

SCIADOPITYS (Umbrella Pine)

Sciadopitys verticillata

SEQUOIA

Sequoia sempervirens (Redwood)
    var. glauca
    var. pendula
Sequoia gigantea (Big Tree) (Wellingtonia)
    var. aurea
    var. glauca
    var. pendula

Foliage of Sequoia

Foliage of Sciadopitys (Umbrella Pine)

TAXUS (Yew)

Taxus baccata (English Yew)
 var. adpressa (Shortleaf English Yew)
 var. adpressa aurea (Golden English Yew)
 var. adpressa erecta (Broom Yew)
 var. adpressa stricta
 var. barroni
 var. cheshuntensis (Cheshunt Yew)
 var. compacta
 var. dovastoni (Dovaston)
 var. dovastoni aureo-variegata (Yellow Dovaston Yew)
 var. elegantissima
 var. epacridioides
 var. erecta
 var. erecta aurea
 var. ericoides
 var. expansa
 var. fastigiata (Irish Yew)
 var. fastigiata aurea (Golden Irish Yew)
 var. fastigiata variegata (Variegated Irish Yew)
 var. glauca
 var. gracilis pendula
 var. imperialis
 var. jacksoni (Jackson Yew)

Taxus baccata—*continued*
 var. lutea
 var. luteobaccata (Yellow Berry Yew)
 var. nana
 var. pyramidalis
 var. recurvata
 var. repandens (Spreading English Yew)
 var. semperaurea
 var. washingtoni (Washington Yew)
 There are varieties grown in Europe in addition to the above.
Taxus brevifolia (Western Yew)
Taxus canadensis (American Yew)
 var. aurea
 var. stricta
Taxus chinensis (Chinese Yew)
Taxus cuspidata (Japanese Yew)
 (Taxus cuspidata *capitata* is frequently used to designate the upright form. Taxus cuspidata indicates the spreading form.)
 var. andersoni (Anderson Yew)
 var. aurescens
 var. browni (Brown's Yew)
 var. densa
 var. intermedia
 var. minima

Foliage of Taxus (yew)

Taxus cuspidata—*continued*
    var. nana (Dwarf Japanese Yew)
    var. thayerae
Taxus media (Middle Yew)
  (This is considered as a hybrid yew by some authorities. Others regard it as a horticultural variety of Taxus cuspidata.)
    var. hatfieldi (Hatfield Yew)
    var. hicksi (Hicks Yew)

TORREYA

Torreya californica (California Nutmeg)
Torreya grandis (Chinese Torreya)
Torreya fargesii (Farges Torreya)
Torreya nucifera (Japanese Torreya)
Torreya taxifolia (Florida Torreya)

Foliage of Torreya

THUYA (Arborvitae)

(Also spelled Thuja)

Thuya koraiensis (Korean Arborvitae)
Thuya occidentalis (American Arborvitae)
    var. alba (Queen Victoria Arborvitae)
    var. aureo-variegata (Goldspot Arborvitae)
    var. batemani (Bateman Arborvitae)
    var. boothi
    var. burrowi
    var. columbia (Columbia Arborvitae)
    var. compacta (Parsons Arborvitae)
    var. conica
    var. cristata (Crested Arborvitae)
    var. densiformia
    var. douglasi aurea (Douglas Golden Arborvitae)

Thuya occidentalis—*continued*
    var. douglasi pyramidalis (Douglas Pyramidal Arborvitae)
  (Considered by some authorities to be the same as Thuya occidentalis spiralis)
    var. dumosa
    var. elegantissima
    var. ellwangeriana
    var. ellwangeriana aurea
    var. ericoides (Heath Arborvitae)
    var. fastigiata
  (Generally known as Thuya occidentalis pyramidalis)
    var. filicoides (Fernleaf Arborvitae)

Thuya (Arborvitae)

Thuya occidentalis—*continued*

    var. filiformis (Threadleaf Arborvitae)

    var. globosa (Globe Arborvitae)

    var. hoopesi

    var. hoveyi (Hovey Arborvitae)

    var. intermedia (Halfhigh Arborvitae)

    var. little gem

    var. lutea (Geo. Peabody Arborvitae)

    var. lutescens

    var. nana (Little Globe Arborvitae)

    var. ohlendorffi

    var. pendula (American Weeping Arborvitae)

    var. plicata (Moss Arborvitae)

    var. pumila (Green Globe Arborvitae)

    var. pygmaea (Pygmy Arborvitae)

    var. pyramidalis (Pyramidal Arborvitae)

    var. recurva nana

    var. reidi (Reid Arborvitae)

    var. riversi (Rivers Arborvitae)

    var. robusta

    (Also known as Thuya occidentalis wareana)

    var. rosenthali (Rosenthal Arborvitae)

    var. semperaurea

    var. smithiana

    var. spaethi (Spath Arborvitae)

    var. spiralis

    var. theodonensis

    var. Tom Thumb

    var. umbraculifera

    var. variegata

    var. vervaeneana (Vervaene Arborvitae)

    var. viridis (American Green Arborvitae)

    var. wagneriana

    var. wareana (Siberian Arborvitae)

    var. woodwardi (Woodward Arborvitae)

Thuya orientalis (Chinese Arborvitae)

    var. argenteo-variegata (Silver Oriental Arborvitae)

    var. aurea (Golden Oriental Arborvitae)

    var. aurea nana (Berckmann Arborvitae)

Thuya orientalis—*continued*

    var. aurea variegata (Goldtwig Arborvitae)

    var. aurea conspicua (Goldspire Arborvitae)

    var. bakeri

    var. beverleyensis

    var. bonita

    var. compacta (Compact Arborvitae)

    var. decussata

    var. elegantissima (Yellow Column Arborvitae)

    var. flagelliformis

    var. funiculata

    var. gracilis (Diana Arborvitae)

    var. intermedia

    var. meldensis

    var. nana compacta

    var. pendula (Weeping Oriental Arborvitae)

    var. pyramidalis (Oriental Pyramidal Arborvitae)

    var. Ramsays Hybrid

    var. Rosedale Hybrid

    var. semperaurescens (Evergolden Arborvitae)

    var. stricta (Also known as Th. or. pyramidalis)

    var. texana glauca

    var. variegata (Variegated Oriental Arborvitae)

    Additional forms exist, chiefly introductions of nurserymen in the South and on the West Coast.

Thuya plicata (Giant Arborvitae)

    var. aurea

    var. fastigiata

    var. pendula

Thuya standishi (Standish Arborvitae)

There is scarcely a variation, however slight, in color, or form or texture of foliage, among the Arborvitaes which has not been responsible for a new variety.

Foliage of Thuyopsis

THUYOPSIS (Hiba-Arborvitae)

Thuyopsis dolabrata
   var. hondai

var. nana
var. variegata

TSUGA (Hemlock)

Tsuga canadensis (Canada Hemlock)
   var. albo-spica (Whitetip Canada
      Hemlock)
   var. atrovirens
   var. aurea
   var. compacta
   var. dawsoniana
   var. fastigiata
   var. fremdi
   var. globosa

var. gracilis
var. hussi
var. jenkinsi
var. macrophylla
var. microphylla
var. nana
var. parvifolia
var. pendula (Sargent Weeping Hemlock)
At the "Hemlock Arboretum," Phila-

Tsuga (Hemlock)—*continued.*

delphia, Mr. Charles F. Jenkins is devoting himself to the unique pastime of studying Hemlocks. Out of this mass of material will no doubt come in the future, many new additions to the Hemlock family.

Tsuga caroliniana (Carolina Hemlock)
Tsuga chinensis (Chinese Hemlock)
Tsuga diversifolia (Japanese Hemlock)
Tsuga dumosa (Himalayan Hemlock)
Tsuga heterophylla (Western Hemlock)
Tsuga mertensiana (Mountain Hemlock)
Tsuga sieboldi (Siebold Hemlock)

Foliage of Tsuga (Hemlock)

PART II

Seed-Collecting, Propagation, Culture, Diseases

Chapter XII

The Flowers of Evergreens

IT is interesting to consider, briefly, the processes of nature which produce seed cones. Flowers of Evergreens are not so conspicuous as are the flowers of the rose or of the apple, for example, nevertheless, this flowering process takes place and is essential to produce fertile seeds.

Two kinds of cones are produced. One is the male or *staminate* cone, which produces the pollen. The male flowers of several species are here illustrated.

The staminate or male flower of the Hemlock shedding pollen. Enlarged about four times. Photograph kindly furnished by Dr. Wm. M. Harlow, New York State College of Forestry, Syracuse, New York.

Picture at right hand is the staminate or male flower of Larch. Picture below is the ovalate or female flower of the Larch. Both enlarged about five times. Photographs kindly furnished by Dr. Wm. M. Harlow, New York State College of Forestry, Syracuse, New York.

The pollen is a yellowish powder, which sometimes falls in great abundance so as to produce a "golden rain," especially in the forests of Evergreens. After the pollen falls, the male cones wither away.

The other cones are the female, seed-bearing cones. They are larger and are woody in structure. When the pollen from the male flowers is released, the scales of the female cone open so that the pollen of the male cone may fall between the scales and fertilize the seed. After this takes place, the scales close and remain thus until the seeds are ripe, when the seeds are set free.

The details vary in different genera and species of Evergreens, both as to appearance of the cones and the time required for maturing. There is also variation in the actual flowering period. The flowers of the Larch bloom early in the spring, sometimes even in late winter. Arborvitae in the vicinity of northern Illinois produce minute flowers in April—the male flowers, pale purple in color; the female flowers, greenish. Redcedars also bloom early, the female flowers of which are almost inconspicuous. These, however, later develop into the small blue berries, which are, botanically, cones.

There are "seed years" and "off" years for most species. Sometimes the "off" years occur over the entire natural range of a species, and sometimes only in certain localities. We have little knowledge of the causes of "seed years" and "off" years. An interval of six or eight "off" years may occur with only a small seed production.

Sometimes a frost or adverse weather conditions at the exact period of pollination will prevent the normal development of seeds. Nature is forever striving to perpetuate each species. It is noticeable that following periods of extreme drought, or of disaster to a tree, an abundance of cones is produced. Old trees which have blown down, and which are barely able to keep alive, will often be almost covered with cones, as if the danger signal had gone out, and a frantic effort were being made to secure posterity for the tree.

Staminate or male flower of Douglas Fir.

Plants such as the

Evergreens, which depend upon the wind to carry pollen, produce it in great abundance. Plants having conspicuous or fragrant flowers attract insects, which are the chief agents in carrying pollen from the male flower to the female flower. Evergreens leave this delicate natural process to the wind.

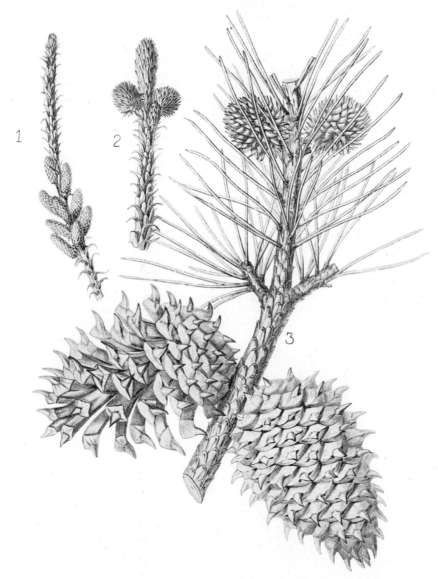

Flowers and cones of the Table Mountain Pine (Pinus pungens). Figure 1 shows the male cones or catkins, which produce the pollen. In figure 2 we see the young female cone. Figure 3 shows the female cones at one year. These are the cones which produce the seed. The matured cones are shown at the base of the branch. One of these is opened as it is when the seed is released, the other still tightly closed. Two years are required from pollination to seed production in most pines. Illustration courtesy Arnold Arboretum, Jamaica Plain, Mass.

Chapter XIII

Cones and Seed

IT is a long, long trail from the Evergreen cones swinging in the breeze, atop some lofty giant of the forest, to the planting of the seed in some far-away nursery.

There is a wide difference in the cones or seed-producing structure of various Evergreens. The largest cones are those of the Sugar Pine, a Pacific coast Evergreen. These measure twelve to twenty inches in length and three to four inches in diameter.* Another Evergreen with large cones is the Coulter Pine. It produces cones ten to fourteen inches long and five to seven inches in diameter.

The size of the cone does not seem to bear any relation to the size of the tree. The Sequoia, or Redwood, while it is among the largest of Evergreens, produces small cones, generally only two to three inches long and 1½ inches in diameter.

Cones are of many shapes and sizes ranging from the jumbo cones of the Sugar Pine, to the small cones of Black Spruce and Hemlock, and the midget cones of the Larch, which are only ⅓ to ⅔ inches long.

Few more delicately and brilliantly-colored objects are found in nature than the cones of Evergreens. In different stages of growth they may be bright yellow and gold, or purple, blue, green, violet, or brown.

Some genera of Evergreens, such as the Cypress family, produce

*See page 261.

Fig. 1. Cypress Cone

Fig. 3. Juniper Berries

Fig. 2. Arborvitae Cones

cones of a totally different appearance, as shown in figure 1. They are more or less round and fastened together in sections, rather than scales, which separate, when ripe, to release the seed.

The cones of the Arborvitae look more like small flower buds, only ⅓ of an inch long in the American Arborvitae. See figure 2.

Junipers produce their seed in the form of berries, which are, botanically, cones. The berries are round, whitish or bluish, sometimes of pinkish tint, usually powdery, and about the size of small currants. The largest Juniper berries are the Syrian Juniper. These berries measure ¾ to one inch in diameter. Most Juniper berries are much smaller, however. The berries require one, two, or three years to mature, depending on the species. The number of seeds contained is variable, ranging from one seed, as in the Cherrystone Juniper, to several, generally two or more, in other species. See figure 3.

The Yews and kindred genera of Evergreens have a still different seed-producing structure, in the form of an ovule or berry-containing seed inset in a bright red (sometimes yellow) cup, open at the top. See figure 4.

Nature has shown a capricious hand in giving distinct characteristics to the various types of cones. Some are persistent; that is, they remain on the trees, unless picked, for as long as six or seven years. Others fall in one or two years. Some open suddenly with an explosion like a small pistol, and scatter their seeds far and wide. Some cones are so tightly closed that they will preserve their seeds through a forest fire.

Fig. 5. Winged Seed

Fig. 4. Longitudinal Section of Yew Berry

The cone itself is only the container for the seed. The scales of the cone remain tightly closed until the proper season, when the scales expand and release the one or more seeds which are stored under the scale. Many species are winged, like the familiar Maple seed, so that the winds can carry them away. See figure 5.

A single ounce of seed of the Giant Redwood, the patriarch of Evergreens, contains about 9,000 seeds. There is scarcely anything in nature which is so interesting to con-

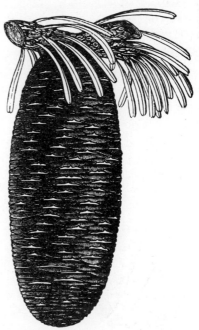

Fir Cone

template as the potential possibilities of life within a single ounce of the seed of this magnificent tree.

The percentage of the seeds produced in the native forests which grow into trees is infinitely small. It is a provision of nature to furnish seed in abundance, so that out of the millions of seeds produced, enough will take root to perpetuate every species.

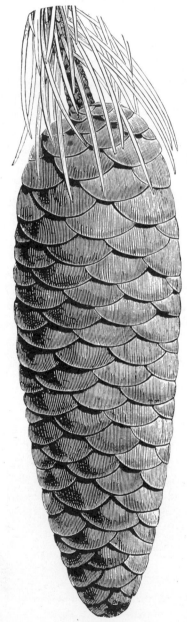

The following figures on the weight of various Evergreen seeds have been taken from "Coniferous Trees" by Webster:

Name of Tree	Number of Seeds per Pound
Abies balsamea (Balsam Fir)	71,100
Abies nordmaniana (Nordman Fir)	9,900
Juniper sabina (Savin Juniper)	2,200
Picea excelsa (Norway Spruce)	68,800
Picea sitchensis (Sitka Spruce)	453,300
Pinus sylvestris (Scotch Pine)	90,600
Pseudotsuga douglassi (Douglas Fir)	95,200
Thuya occidentalis (American Arborvitae)	186,600
Tsuga canadensis (Hemlock)	210,000

Edible Pine Seeds

Numerous species of Pines throughout the world, called the Nut Pines, furnish edible seeds, which are important items of food in many localities. The Pinyon Pine, a native of the southwest, furnishes a principal item in the diet of the Indians. Many seeds of lesser size are eaten both as a food and as a confection in various parts of the world.

Spruce Cone

Hemlock Cone

Chapter XIV

Evergreen Seed Collecting

THE search for Evergreen seed leads to many distant lands, into the deep forests, to the hills and mountains, far from the comforts of home. A seed-collector goes on horseback with saddle bags, on a lonely journey from Flagstaff, Arizona, nearly two hundred miles into the San Francisco mountains to seek the seed of the beautiful and elusive Cork Fir. Only in a small tract of mountain wilds is this tree found.

Far up on the treacherous crags of the Alps a race of dwarf Pines struggles for life. From these trees the cones of the Dwarf Mugho Pine are gathered.

In the hills of sunny Italy the berries of the Savin Juniper are picked and cleaned and started on their long journey. In South Dakota, in the haunting caverns of the Black Hills, old prospectors search out the berries of the Silver Juniper.

Japan is one of the richest fields for Evergreen seed. There, in abundance, are Firs, Yews, and Spruces that each year yield an important contribution in seeds.

That great and mysterious land of China provides many treasures for seed-collectors. Tons of seed are each year carried thousands of miles on the backs

How strange it is that out of these barren hills can spring trees of such beauty! In such surroundings as these unfruitful cliffs and ravines in the Black Hills of South Dakota is the home of the Silver Juniper.

69

Forest ranger picking Yellow Pine cones in Cochetopa National Forest, Colorado. These pickers average about eight bushels per day. Photo by U. S. Forest Service.

of coolies to some seaport to reach the nurseries of other parts of the world.

From the Black Forest of Germany, the rugged hills of Scandanavia, and the wide expanses of Russia, Evergreen seeds are gathered.

The Rocky Mountains, the Pacific Coast range, Minnesota, Wisconsin, and Michigan are all drawn upon.

In all, there is scarcely a country of the world overlooked. Where to look, and when to gather, must be thoroughly understood. Seed-collectors must make no mistakes in identifying the trees. The network of seed-collectors covers the world. No locality is too far away; no spot, too difficult to reach, for these gatherers of the seed.

In collecting Evergreen seed, it is the cones which must be gathered. The seed is extracted

The late Ernest H. Wilson kindly supplied this photograph representing conditions under which the plant hunter lives. This photograph was made in the most remote section of Korea.

later by various methods. A bushel of cones produces only a small amount of seed. Some average yields of seed per bushel of cones, are as follows:

Sugar Pine	1½ lbs.
Douglas Fir	1¼ lbs.
White Pine	1 lb.
Western Larch	½ lb.
Lodge-Pole Pine	¼ lb.

Seed prices vary according to the scarcity of the seed, the demand, the difficulty of collecting, whether hand-picked or otherwise, the percentage of purity, and the germination test. $1.00 to $10.00 per pound covers the usual price range, although much higher prices may be paid for some unusual or very scarce sorts.

The precarious life of a seed gatherer in Angeles National Forest, California. Photo by Scudder, Courtesy U. S. Forest Service.

Gathering cones from a squirrel hoard. Nearly five pounds of clean seed obtained from this one hoard. Photo by W. D. Hayes, Courtesy U. S. Forest Service.

The time to collect is when the seed is mature. The time, of course, varies with the particular species, the latitude of its production, and the special seasonal conditions. A variation of two weeks in ripening time may occur in the same area from year to year.

There are three ways of collecting. Certain trees shed their cones without opening, and these may be gathered from the ground. Cones may be hand-picked by climbing the trees and cutting the cones with various long-handled hooks or cutters. Most cones are cut and stored in hoards, by squirrels and chipmunks. The little animals easily reach the topmost branches where the cones are most plentiful. They have an uncanny judgment concerning just when to cut the cones. Some squirrels do the cutting, and others carry the cones into any suitable place they can find to store them. Frequently ten to fifteen bushels will be stored in a ravine or hollow, or sometimes on the level ground, where they are carefully hidden with leaves or grass.

Squirrels are careful to store the cones with the scales pointed downward to shed water. Only cones with good seed are collected, and almost invariably each species is stored separately. Incidentally, many of these buried cones are never dug up, and seedlings thus get an easy start.

These hoards of cones are often difficult to locate, and it is safe to say that not ten per cent of the squirrels' food is thus stolen from them. They cut and store many times more cones than they can use; so there is no great injustice imposed on these little animals by the seed-collectors.

Most cones must be cured and then heated in order to expand the scales and release the

Yellow Pine being treated in preparation for field sowing. Lolo National Forest, Montana. Photo by E. C. Clifford, Courtesy U. S. Forest Service.

Branchlet of Pine with ripe cone.

seed. Where collecting is done far from transportation, the cones may be spread out on wire screens, or on canvas, and exposed to the heat of the sun. In three to fourteen days the cones will open. Then the cones must be raked, or flailed, or shaken, to release the seed. Various contrivances are used, some of which are here illustrated. Often the cones are stored over winter and placed in a drying kiln in the spring. Where seed extraction is done on a large scale, special buildings are constructed, with bins for curing, and artificial heat for opening.

When the seed is extracted it will contain two to five times its bulk in foreign matter, such as wings, twigs, resin, and cone fragments. The seed is rubbed through a screen, or gently flailed, or turned in a canvas, or poured from one vessel to another. There are also mechanical devices with the fanning mill principle to clean seed.

When finally cleaned and ready, the seed requires special conditions for storing, to retain its vitality. When properly stored in glass jars, seed may be kept over for more than one year.

When a species of Evergreen grows over a considerable range of latitude and altitude, it is important to obtain seed from certain specified localities. Because of the variation in the hardiness and rapidity of growth, seed from certain districts is much more valuable. Seed of many varieties, used in the Hill Nursery, is, therefore, gathered by direct supervision, rather than purchased in the open market.

Screening cones of Engelmann Spruce. This separates much dirt that would have to be taken out in a final cleaning.

Extracting seed. Winged seed taken from under shaker and brought together in a heap. Photo by Smith Riley, Courtesy U. S. Forest Service.

CHAPTER XV

Methods of Propagating Evergreens

THESE remarks are only in the nature of a definition of the different methods of propagation and a brief outline of the steps in each process. The actual technical procedure requires special study and long experience. A plan followed with one variety does not always work with another. There is a big difference between explaining "how it is done," and giving the actual rules of "how to do it." Such information is covered in various books on the subject of propagation.

There are four methods by which Evergreens are usually propagated; namely: (1) seeds, (2) cuttings, (3) grafts, (4) layers.

The method of reproduction is not so much a matter of choice, as of necessity. Propagation from seed is preferable when practicable. Only those trees which are natives, or which grow wild in nature, and which produce seeds, can be propagated from seed. All horticultural varieties, which were originally variations from some native species, must be grown by artificial methods.

For example, if matured seeds developed on a horticultural variety (as they frequently do) and the seeds were planted, the resulting trees might bear little resemblance to their parents. If we plant the seed from a golden Arborvitae, a mixture of forms would likely result. On the other hand, when grown from cuttings or grafts, the peculiar characteristics of the parent tree will almost invariably be reproduced in the offspring. Trueness to type is thus better insured. Some sorts can be grown either from cuttings or grafts. Others do not make a good root growth from cuttings and should be grafted.

The exact procedure to follow is a matter of individual skill and experience. Under favorable conditions, on a small scale, where every detail can be controlled, it is frequently possible to accomplish a result in propagation which could not be undertaken successfully on a large scale production. Climatic conditions also have a great influence. A system which may work in one locality will often fail somewhere else.

PROPAGATION FROM SEEDS

The propagation of Evergreens is considered one of the most difficult of any order of plants, especially in the northern part of the United States where the winters are severely cold and the summers may be hot and dry.

Warmth and moisture are the first necessities to germinate seeds. The period

74

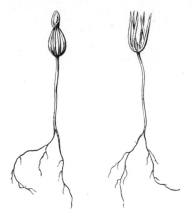

Small seedlings shortly after germination.

Spruce seedlings two years old.

immediately following germination is the critical time. The little plants are most sensitive and may easily succumb to any excess of heat, moisture or dampness. The period of germination differs widely among various species. Some will start to sprout in a few days, continuing for thirty days. Others will require as much as three months. Unless the seed is especially prepared, some seeds will lie a whole year before coming up.

Evergreen seedlings are usually grown out-of-doors in beds, although sometimes in boxes, in greenhouses. The preparation of the soil is much the same as would be the case when preparing a bed for a vegetable garden. Planting is usually done in the spring as soon as the ground is in a workable condition, which may be any time from the last of March until the first of May, depending upon the locality. The exact dimensions of the bed are matters of choice. A convenient size is to make the beds three or four feet across and of a length to suit the extent of the planting.

The seed is usually planted by hand-broadcast in the beds, although some planters prefer to plant in rows. The amount of seed is a matter entirely dependent upon the quality of seed and the variety of the tree. Seed which proves to be only fifty percent fertile needs to be planted thicker than seed showing a higher test. The amount of seed also varies with the variety. About the only general rule that could be given is to plant the seed too thick rather than too thin. Immediately after the seed is sown, a light covering of sand or sandy loam should be sprinkled over the bed and then packed down with a light roller or the back of a spade.

Birds are very fond of the small seedlings when the latter first push through the soil, carrying the seed on their heads. Mice and rodents also are apt to prove a nuisance.

Some planters prefer to cover the beds with cheese cloth, which is kept on during the day and removed at night, until the trees have reached one inch or more in height. Other planters use a high shade made of lath, or brush, six feet high, over the beds as a protection from the sun. Other planters use shades of lath set close to the ground, at a height of only a few inches, allowing this lath to remain on the beds the first season. The lath-shade is constructed with spaces left between the lath so that only one-half of the bed is shaded at once.

Seedling beds in the Hill Nursery.

Frequent watering is important when the season is dry. Cultivation and weeding must be attended to if the seedlings are to make a satisfactory growth. Seedlings should remain in the beds two years. Some slow-growers are left for three years before transplanting. If left in the beds longer than three years, the roots become too coarse.

Two year old seedlings in the Hill Nursery from which the lath shades have been removed.

Propagation from "Cuttings"

This process is familiar to almost every one who has taken "slips" or cuttings of geraniums and other house plants. A small twig, or branchlet, is cut from the mother plant and by various means is induced to take root. Because of the slow growth and the resinous sap of Evergreens, this process is not so easily carried out as it might seem. The growth is so slow in some species of Evergreens that propagation by cuttings is not practicable. In other species the growth is comparatively rapid. Some few varieties in very mild climates will take root when planted in soil in the nursery rows. The great majority, however, are grown either in hotbeds or in greenhouses.

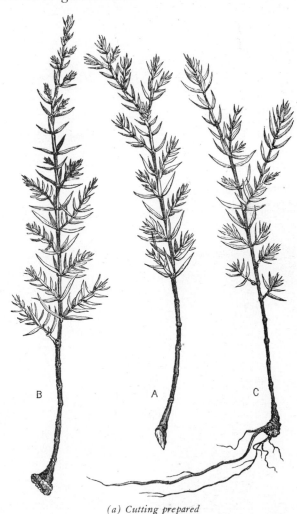

Soft wood or green wood cuttings are taken in the summer time when the tree is still growing and is in soft growth. These cuttings are planted in hotbeds, prepared according to different systems, with manure, sand, and soil. Glass sash is often used on the beds and provision made to shade the beds from severe sun. Only a limited number of varieties are grown in this way. Most cuttings are "hard wood" cuttings.

Hardwood cuttings are taken in the late fall or early winter. They are planted in boxes, in sand, or in various mixtures of soil, sand, and fertilizers, and kept in a greenhouse. The drawing on this page shows the size and shape of the cutting when cut, the beginning of the callus, the soft spongy growth at the end of the cutting, and the formation of the first roots.

(a) Cutting prepared
(b) Cutting callused
(c) The roots forming

Many weeks, and even a year, may be required for rooting to take place. Some conditions of temperature or moisture will frequently spell failure to the whole operation. Some trees root easily; others, only with the greatest difficulty.

Even among those long-experienced in growing Evergreens from cuttings, new ideas are always being tried. Would you take cuttings from the lower branches, the side branches or the top branches? Would you make the cutting in summer or winter? Would you take a straight cutting, a heel-cutting (with the joint attached where the branchlet grew onto the larger branch), or would you make

a mallet-cutting? Whichever your choice might be, you would find plenty of supporters for any plan. It is of first importance to select trees of the best type, those of finest form or color. Secondly, it is important to establish roots on the cutting by whatever devices you may command.

*Upper picture shows interior of a cutting house at the Hill Nursery. Lower picture shows
men engaged in making Evergreen grafts.*

GROWING EVERGREENS FROM GRAFTS

The process of grafting Evergreens is one of the most complicated of propagating problems. It is possible sometimes to graft outdoors, but practically all Evergreen-grafting is done in a greenhouse. Trees may generally be developed with a greater saving of time by grafting than by other methods. Briefly, the process is one by which a cut branch called a cion or scion, of the tree to be propagated, is united to the stem of a seedling, called an understock. There are numerous kinds of grafts or incisions made in grafting various kinds of plants, such as the cleft-graft, tongue-graft, saddle-graft, and side-graft.

The side-graft is customarily used in grafting Evergreens. The drawing below shows the nature of the scion and the style of the cut at the time of making the graft. Variations in detail are practiced by nurserymen in making grafts. The principle, however, is the same in each case.

In selecting the understock it is best to use the same family for an understock as the scion. For example, Firs are grafted on Fir seedlings, Spruces, on Spruce seedlings, etc. Two or three-year-old seedlings are taken up in the fall and planted in small pots. These are put in a warm greenhouse and in a few weeks start to make a new growth. In early winter the scions are cut, and the actual

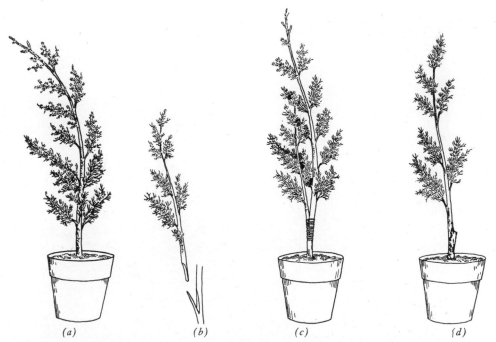

(a) (b) (c) (d)

(a) Juniper understock in pot. (b) The scion and method of grafting it to the understock (c) Grafting operations completed. The scion securely tied to the understock. (d) Several weeks later the understock cut away showing the scion, which has taken the root of the understock.

Juniper grafts.

grafting takes place. The scions are tied in place with string, or raffia, or rubber bands. Soon the wound will callus, or heal over, and the scion will take up sap from the seedling and start to grow. At the proper time, the top of the seedling is cut away and the scion then becomes the top for the seedling, functioning thereafter as a natural tree.

This surgical operation on the tree is a delicate process which must be performed with due regard to the peculiar characteristics of each individual variety. Conditions of moisture, nourishment, and heat make all the difference between success and failure. Green-

Interior of an Evergreen grafting house.

houses where grafting is done are of peculiar construction. The benches are covered with glass sash during certain periods to develop the proper humidity.

GROWING EVERGREENS FROM LAYERS

This process is not practiced on any extensive scale, nor is it usable except with certain low-growing trees, whose branches are on, or near, the ground. Two methods may be employed. One method is to throw a mound of earth over the ends of the lower branches of the tree and leave it there until the branches take root. Then the rooted branches are cut off and transplanted.

The other method is to pin an individual branch to the ground covering it with soil but leaving the end of the branch exposed. Under favorable conditions the branch will, in time, throw out roots. The branch then is cut off and transplanted. Obviously this system requires a type of low-branched tree.

This method is also used in the propagation of other kinds of trees and shrubs. In growing Evergreens from layers, the trees most frequently grown are such trees as Pfitzer Juniper, Savin Juniper, and some of the creeping forms of Junipers. While it is a successful method under some conditions, it is not a practical plan for commercial production on a large scale.

Pine grafts after the understock has been removed.

CHAPTER XVI

Root-Pruning and Transplanting

WHEN an Evergreen starts to grow, it pushes its roots down into the soil as deeply and as quickly as possible. This is the natural tendency of a tree. The longer a tree stands, the coarser the roots grow, and the deeper they go into the ground. If the tree is never going to be moved, we can forget the need of root-pruning and transplanting. But when Evergreens are to be sold and moved, there is work to be done by the nurseryman, operations that do not show when you look at the tree, because the roots, of course, are underground.

Fig. 1. *The formation of roots before root pruning.*

Let us look at the drawing in figure 1, particularly at the roots. Any one can see it would be almost impossible to dig such a tree, and save all the roots. Many of the roots would be cut off, so that when the tree is moved, there would not be enough roots to support the top. Then one of two things happens. Either the tree will die, or it will be so weak that it will take two or three years to get over the shock. In the meantime, it will become weak and thin. That is why the system of

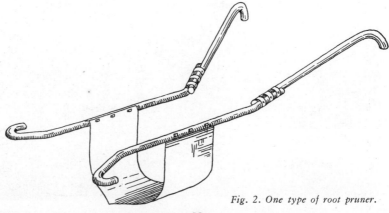

Fig. 2. *One type of root pruner.*

root-pruning and transplanting, as practiced by the leading nurseries, is of utmost importance.

Root-pruning and transplanting are expensive operations, requiring special equipment. On a small scale, root-pruning may be done by cutting around the tree and under the tree with a sharp spade. When performed on a large scale, a U-shaped, steel blade is pulled along under the row of trees with a tractor, or, when working on large trees, by running a cable on a drum at the end of the row. Figure 2 shows a root-pruner of the type described.

This process does not improve the appearance of the top of the tree. On the contrary, trees never root-pruned will generally have a more perfect shape and fuller foliage, for the reason that they have never had their growth disturbed. Neglect of this unseen nursery operation is responsible for the majority of failures which occur in Evergreen-planting. Lack of root-pruning is, incidentally, the reason why wild trees taken from the woods seldom grow when transplanted. Unfortunately, many nurserymen do not recognize the vital importance of this operation, or they neglect it through lack of necessary money and equipment. Insist that the trees you buy have been root-pruned and transplanted! Nursery firms who specialize in Evergreens, and whose trees live and quickly establish themselves, make root-pruning and transplanting the most important operation of their nursery work. Transplanting is done separately, apart from the root-pruning process. Trees are taken up from one part of the nursery and replanted, generally into wider rows.

When Evergreen seedlings, cuttings, or grafts are two years old, the trans-

Fig. 3. Evergreens in transplant bed.

Fig. 4. Fine fibrous roots on small transplanted Evergreens.

planting begins. Such trees are planted in beds, never remaining more than two years. After two years, many fine, fibrous roots have formed, but the coarse roots have not had a chance to develop. Sometimes these trees are again put back in beds where they remain two years more. There is little, if any, actual pruning or cutting of the roots that takes place at this stage, because the process of digging the trees and disturbing the roots causes the tree to throw out a new

Fig. 5. The second period of transplanting into field rows.

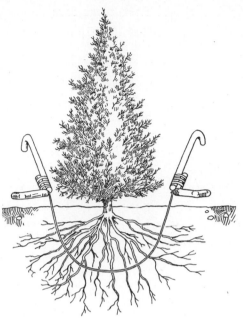

Fig. 6. Position of root pruner in pruning roots.

Fig. 7. Root system after pruning has been done.

set of fine roots. Figure 3 shows trees in transplanted bed.

By this period the trees have developed a fibrous root system. (See figure 4.) The minute, hair-like fibers are the important part of the tree's roots. These are the feeding tendrils that readily take up nourishment and moisture. The coarse, heavy, woody parts of the root only serve to anchor the tree, and to conduct the food and water into the tissues of the tree.

By the time the tree has had one, or perhaps two, growing periods of at least two-year's duration each, in beds, it is ready for nursery rows. Here it remains for another two years. It is necessary to allow two-year intervals, so as to give the top time to grow also. The first year after the transplanting takes place, most of the energy of the tree goes into root growth. The second year the top growth shows greater development.

Fig. 8. Root growth one year after root pruning.

Fig. 9. Digging with solid earth ball.

Figure 5 shows Evergreens after they have passed their period of growth in beds and are planted out in field rows.

After two years in field rows, the process of root-pruning begins. Figure 6 shows how the root-pruner operates. Figure 7 shows how the root-pruner actually cuts off the coarse roots. Figure 8 represents the tree one year later, with a new mass of fibrous roots.

Root-pruning, or transplanting, continues at two-year intervals during the entire time the tree remains in the nursery. It is not unusual to perform these operations six or eight times in well-conducted nurseries. When the time comes for the tree to be delivered to the customer, it is dug with an earth ball. This is another most important process. If the transplanting has been carried on as described, the tree can be dug with the roots undisturbed, with all the important roots still attached to the tree. If half of the roots are chopped off, and the dirt shovelled loosely into the burlap, only a miracle can make the tree grow.

"B&B," a term widely used in Evergreen growing, should mean that the tree

Fig. 10. Evergreens in field rows, three to four times transplanted.

is dug with the same earth in which it grew, and the earth ball then wrapped in burlap. A big earth ball does not necessarily mean an abundance of roots. The more compact and fibrous the roots, the smaller the earth ball needs to be.

The life of an Evergreen in the nursery is one of frequent change. Trees only three to four feet high represent at least ten years of nursery care. Larger trees may easily be fifteen to twenty years old when delivered to the customer. The process for developing roots, as described, is only one-half of the picture. There is the cultivating, the trimming or shaping of the tree, the staking to develop a straight leader, the fertilizing, the spraying, and the many other frequent attentions that are necessary to produce choice, attractive, specimen Evergreens.

"What a strange underground life is that which is led by the organisms we call trees! These great fluttering masses of leaves, stems, boughs, trunks, are not the real tree. They live underground and what we see are nothing more than their tails."

—OLIVER WENDELL HOLMES.

Fig. 11: When properly root pruned and transplanted it is possible to dig Evergreens with all the important roots contained in a ball such as this.

Fig. 12. Choice Evergreens must be staked and trimmed, as well as frequently transplanted and root pruned to produce specimens of the finest quality.

CHAPTER XVII

Suggestions on How to Plant Evergreens

"Before the young planter set foot upon the spade, we beg leave to caution him in the strongest terms against a WANT OF SPIRIT in planting. A slovenly planter ranks among the most extravagant order of slovens. The labor, the plants and the ground are thrown away."

—"Planting and Rural Ornament."

THIS admonition written in the 18th century is just as good advice today. It well points out that thoroughness in every detail is the keynote of successful planting.

PLANTING BALLED-AND-BURLAPPED EVERGREENS

"Balled-and-Burlapped" means that the tree is dug from the nursery soil with the earth remaining undisturbed about the roots of the tree. The earth ball is securely wrapped in burlap and tied with stout rope. The tops of all except the small trees are tied up to prevent injury to the branches. This method practically insures safe handling and very little shock to the tree in moving.

It is advisable to plant your Evergreens as soon as they are received. If impossible to do this, they will keep for several days in good condition if earth balls are kept from drying out. If unable to plant at once, submerge each earth ball in a tub of water for a few minutes. Then stand the tree in a place out of the wind and sun.

Leave the limbs tied up and the burlap on the roots until after the trees are planted.

Dig the holes somewhat wider and deeper than necessary to easily admit the earth ball. Set the tree straight, and an inch or two deeper than it stood in the nursery. (You can tell by the soil line on the stem.)

Leave the burlap around the earth ball, but cut the string and lay back the burlap as shown in sketch. (The burlap helps to anchor the tree and soon rots away.)

Tamp the loose dirt in firmly, bearing your whole weight to pack it in tightly. When the hole is two-thirds filled, flood with water, and then draw in enough loose dirt to level off the ground.

After the tree is planted, unwind the string from the top and carefully straighten out the branches.

The foregoing remarks cover the various simple steps of the actual planting. We wish, however, to call attention to other details which properly must be considered in planting.

SOIL. It is assumed that the planting site and soil conditions are favorable. In Chapter 19 are some suggestions on preparing soil.

FERTILIZER. There is more and more attention being given to proper feeding of

Before digging holes it is a good plan to arrange the trees in position. Sometimes, in this way, an improvement in arrangement will suggest itself. Move the trees around until the most attractive setting is found.

Evergreens. We recommend the use of Hill Evergreen Tree Food, a scientifically prepared, balanced ration for Evergreens. Please refer to Chapter 21 for a detailed discussion of different fertilizer materials.

PEAT MOSS. In recent years there has been an increasing use of peat moss in planting and mulching Evergreens. Peat moss is of inestimable benefit in many ways. It may be mixed with heavy soil, it promotes fibrous root growth, and it retains moisture. The merits of peat moss are more fully covered in Chapter 20.

AFTER CARE. Watering, cultivating, pruning, and other cultural directions are fully discussed elsewhere in this book.

TRANSPLANTING SMALL EVERGREENS

By *small* Evergreens we mean seedlings, or small transplanted Evergreens which are handled in the same manner as seedlings. Seedlings and small transplanted sizes are intended for transplanting into a bed or nursery, to be cultivated for a few years until large enough to handle. They are not expected to be used in their permanent locations.

One important fact to learn in handling small Evergreens is to keep the roots of the trees moist. Unlike shrubs and other deciduous nursery stock which can be placed in storage, *the roots of Evergreens must always be protected from the air and sun.* Failure to observe this fact does more to diminish good results than any other one cause. Evergreen trees have thick, resinous sap, which dries up and hardens when the roots are exposed to the action of the wind and sun, resulting in the loss of the trees.

It is not practical to attempt transplanting Evergreens less than two inches high. It is obvious that trees so small and delicate must be handled with excellent care, and even then there is a great risk in handling. The best size of seedlings is four to six, and six to eight inches. The trees reach the planter from the nursery, graded in a uniform size, and tied in bundles of fifty. The roots are packed in damp moss, which retains moisture, and the trees should arrive in the hands of the planter in fine condition. The planting instructions which follow, apply equally to seedlings and small, transplanted seedlings, cuttings, or grafts.

INSTRUCTIONS FOR PLANTING

The ground should be ready for planting before the trees arrive. Where circumstances prevent previous preparation, provision must be made to take care of the trees until the ground can be prepared for planting.

Where there is a delay of only a day or two, the seedlings can remain in the boxes without injury until ready to plant. *The boxes should be kept in a cool place out of reach of the sun and wind.*

Where Evergreens are received with the roots "Puddled," or covered with a coating of mud, this should be washed off before planting.

If the planting cannot be done for several days, the seedlings must be removed from the boxes and trenched or "heeled in" in some protected spot until planting can be taken care of. In trenching the trees, first dip the roots in water until thoroughly moist, and then dig a small trench, covering the roots with fine, loose dirt and packing the dirt in firmly. Where sand is available, this makes good material to use for trenching. They can remain in this condition for several days.

Plant in Beds

The best practice in handling small Evergreens, based on many years' experience, is to plant in beds as shown in the sketches herewith. The advantage of planting in beds is easily seen. It is easy to provide the necessary shade the first year, space is conserved, and trees are handy for cultivation and watering.

By using a board six feet long and three or four inches wide, a straight row is easily laid out. With a sharp spade, dig a trench as shown. Plant the trees, spreading the roots out carefully and immediately filling in with dirt. It is important that the small evergreens be planted about the same depth as in the nursery. This depth is easily determined from the stem of the tree.

When the first row is planted, proceed as shown, in cutting the next trench. While it not only makes straight rows of uniform space this method allows the roots to be spread out without crowding. Where the roots are crowded into small holes in poorly prepared soil, it cannot be expected that the growth will be anything but slow and disappointing.

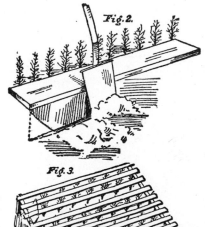

When the planting is completed as shown in figure three, a shade should be immediately constructed and placed in position to protect the trees from the severe sun the first season. This lath shade should be set on stakes and elevated 8 or 10 inches above the top of the seedlings.

Space should be left between the lath as shown so the shade will not be too heavy. An opening equal to the width of one lath is recommended so the shade covers only one-half of the bed at one time.

The beds usually are made six feet wide and the trees planted about six inches apart. This will allow twelve trees for each row in the bed. The distance may be increased or decreased, depending on the varieties being planted, and how long it is intended that the trees will remain in the beds.

On page 91 is illustrated a simple system for planting seedlings and other small Evergreens.

Special Instructions for Planting Grafts

The general directions for planting, as given above, may be followed in planting grafts. It is important, however, to carefully remove the string which binds the graft, as this will cut into the stem of the graft as it starts to grow.

Transplanting Small Evergreens in the Commercial Nursery

Where large quantities of seedlings are to be planted in a nursery, these further suggestions are given.

In nurseries, beds usually run from fifty to one hundred feet long, and six feet wide. In constructing the racks for shade, the usual plan is to drive wooden posts at the four corners of the bed, with smaller posts at intervals along the sides. A wire, stretched along the top of these posts, will provide a framework on which to lay the lath racks. This wire should be twelve to eighteen inches above the ground, depending upon the size of the trees used, and how long they are to remain in the beds.

In constructing the racks, it will be found more satisfactory, and easier to handle them, if the lath racks are made with the lath running lengthwise of the bed rather than crosswise. A four-foot lath, cut once in two, will give a two-foot length which, when built on to a framework, makes a much more rigid rack, and one which can easily be removed for watering and cultivating. Such a rack will last for a number of seasons, where those made with long lengths of lath and laid crosswise of the bed, are more easily damaged in handling.

Where considerable planting is to be done, the use of a "planting-board" will be found a great convenience and economy. By this method, an entire row may be planted at once. See photograph of planting-board on page 93.

It might also be said that the *lath-shading* is not always necessary in planting some of the larger transplanted sizes. On the other hand, some varieties of Evergreens, such as Yews and Hemlocks, show better results when the shading is continued for several years, even after they have passed through this first transplanting stage.

Preparing the Soil

A location should be selected where the soil is well-drained, loose and workable, open to the full sun.

The ground should be worked-up, spaded and raked thoroughly; when planting is done on a large scale, plow deeply, pulverizing and rolling with proper machinery. If possible, it is of good advantage to have the ground prepared several months in advance. Turn the ground over to a good depth several times during the previous season. The soil will then work up freely in the spring, and planting will be done much easier. The dirt will pack in around the roots of the trees in good shape and go a long way toward insuring a successful planting. Thorough preparation of the soil cannot be over-estimated. Where well-rotted manure is available, this can be applied in limited quantity on top of the ground before the spading begins, and thoroughly worked into the soil. Great care should be taken, however, to see that no green manure is used, or other fertilizer, the action of which might be too severe on the little trees. (See chapter 21 for detailed information on fertilizers.)

Small Evergreens will grow in any loose, well-drained ground; but, if there is any choice of ground available, select that which is free from stones or other objectionable material, and where the soil is loose, and drainage is good.

PLANTING

Pack the soil firmly about the roots, pressing down with the foot, and bearing the entire weight of the body to set them firmly. "Stepping-in" is the usual nursery term for this operation.

The board is here filled ready to place in position to plant setting 12 trees at one time. As many as 35 smaller trees can be planted if all the notches are used.

CULTURAL SUGGESTIONS

No matter how carefully you follow instructions for planting, it is of no purpose, if cultivation and watering are neglected. In a well-kept nursery, small, transplanted Evergreens are kept cultivated constantly. Every bed is hand-cultivated six or eight times during the summer, or as often as necessary, to keep

This is the last operation. The board is in place and the dirt partly filled in. The board is then removed and made ready for the next row. Two or more planting-boards are necessary to keep the planters going; one board is filled while the other one is engaged in planting.

the ground loose and the weeds out. Cultivation must be kept up, and the trees watered, if the season is very dry. It is better to cultivate often and water less frequently. It is not so much the amount of water which is used on the trees, as to retain the water in the ground by maintaining a high state of cultivation and preserving the moisture.

In nurseries, the use of a sprinkling system reduces the possibility of loss through drought. Even a sprinkling system does not take the place of cultivation and weeding. The weeding, of course, must be done by hand with a very small, narrow hoe or rake many times during each season.

RIGHT WAY

This picture illustrates the proper sized hole for planting small Evergreens. Make the holes large enough so that the roots may be spread out, in order to take their moisture from a larger area. Trees planted in this way make a rapid and thrifty growth.

THE PLANTING-BOARD FOR EXTENSIVE PLANTINGS

Various types of planting-boards are in use in nurseries, as a means of saving time in planting operations. The use of such a device gives a uniform planting distance and is a great labor and time saver where there are large numbers of trees to handle. The board shown on page 93 is made of two pieces, six feet long, the lower piece notched and the two pieces hinged together.

INSTRUCTIONS FOR TWICE-TRANSPLANTED EVERGREENS

Trees referred to in these instructions are small sizes, usually not more than twelve or eighteen inches in height, such as are usually planted out in nursery rows.

One important thing to remember in planting trees without earth ball is to avoid exposing the roots to the sun and wind. Trees without a protection of dirt on the roots easily suffer from drying out; so it is important to keep the trees in the box until ready to plant, or to cover the roots with a piece of wet burlap, or in some way to keep the roots damp, and protected from the air.

Needless to say, Evergreens, the same as other crops, will repay you in thrifty growth for thorough preparation of the soil.

Soil must be thoroughly prepared and in a fine and mellow condition. Dig the holes so that there is plenty of room for the natural spread of the roots, as indicated in the two photographs shown.

Sift the fine dirt around the roots, allowing them to spread out in a natural way, and pack the dirt in firmly.

4 to 5 years old once trans-planted

WRONG WAY

Trees planted in holes tapering to the bottom, as in this illustration, and with the roots matted together, have a great handicap to overcome in trying to become established. Contrast this sort of planting with that shown on opposite page.

5 to 7 years old twice trans-planted

Trees can then be watered, filling up the holes with as much water as will soak into the ground, and then placing a mulch of fine dirt around the trees. A few days after planting, they should again be watered. This watering and cultivation should continue frequently during the first spring and summer, or until the plants are established.

FERTILIZER. For complete information on fertilizer refer to chapter 21.

MOVING LARGE EVERGREENS

Trees which have been originally planted too close together will often reach a point where they must be moved if the trees are to be preserved, or it is sometimes possible to buy large trees, either from a nursery or from some private grounds, and thus save many years in waiting for a tree to grow. We refer to trees fifteen to twenty-five feet or larger.

It is not so much a question of whether trees can be moved successfully or not, but a problem of the equipment necessary and the expense of moving.

Nurserymen who make a specialty of moving large trees are equipped with necessary platforms, wagons, and tackle; and, where the trees are large and valuable, a professional tree mover should be engaged. The precaution necessary to take in moving large trees depends upon the type of tree to be moved, its size, the soil in which it is growing, and the general health and thriftiness of the tree.

Sometimes a special root-pruning process two years in advance is advisable. This is done by digging a ditch two or three feet wide, around the tree, at a distance proportionate to its size, cutting through all the side roots, leaving the tap root, if any, intact, filling the ditch with rich garden soil or loam, and keeping it well-watered. At the same time the tree must be suitably braced to prevent blowing over. New feeding roots will be established in the rich mold, so that when the tree is ready to take up with an earth ball, it has already a sufficient quantity of new fibrous roots to insure its successful growth after being transplanted. This practice is very seldom carried out with Evergreens, but is merely mentioned to show precaution which could be taken if necessary, in case a tree appears to be of low vitality and might not otherwise stand moving.

Most big tree moving is done during the winter with a frozen ball of earth. The secret of success is to dig the tree with as many of its roots as possible, and to deliver it to its new location with the earth ball around it, unbroken, and the roots kept from sun and wind.

Where it can be determined in advance of the winter season, it is a considerable saving of time and energy if both the ground to which the tree is to be moved, as well as the soil around the tree itself, can be covered with a mulch of leaves, hay, etc., to prevent its freezing. This will greatly facilitate the work of digging during the winter, when the ground is frozen.

In the case of medium sized trees, which anyone desires to move from one part of the grounds to another, that is, trees up to 10 or 12 feet in height, all the above equipment and labor is not necessary. All that needs to be done is to dig the tree with as large an earth ball as seems necessary to move it successfully. Transplanting, if done properly, does not carry any great risk on the life of the tree.

The above interesting old illustration of tree moving was taken from a book published in 1794 entitled, "A Practical Treatise on Planting and the Management of Woods and Coppices," published by the Dublin Society.

Figure 1. Shows the pole divided at the end, and inserted into the axle tree, with the hollowed piece of timber over it.

Figure 2. Represents the machine brought close over the root of the tree, and the pole tied up along the stem.

Figure 3. Shows the manner in which the root will fit between the wheels; when the pole has been drawn down, the little wheel behind may be used by inserting its frame into the pole, but except for very large trees and such as are to be carried a considerable distance, there is no occasion for this third wheel.

CHAPTER XVIII

Transplanting Season

LEST we be contradicted by experienced planters, we acknowledge that under favorable conditions, it is possible to transplant Evergreens any day during the year. We do not wish to advocate such a plan, especially with trees taken up and shipped. On the other hand, where small or medium-sized trees are to be merely transplanted to a different part of the grounds, the transplanting can be successfully done almost any time, with proper precaution, except during the very hottest days of the summer.

From the practical standpoint, there are only two safe seasons to plant Evergreens, a few weeks in the spring and a few weeks in the fall. We are speaking now of conditions in the north central states. For planters who live in Florida, California, or other localities where the seasons are not so well defined as they are here in northern Illinois, planting time may continue from late in the fall, until February or March, in the spring.

In certain localities some planting is done in late August. Such advice, frequently given in magazine articles and elsewhere, may be followed in sections where extremely hot, dry weather does not prevail in August.

SPRING PLANTING SEASON

In the latitude of Chicago, it is usually the first of April before the ground is in condition to plant Evergreens in the spring. Some years, we are able to plant the last of March, and again the season may not open until early in April. On the whole, however, we can say from the first of April until the 15th of May is the proper time to plant Evergreens in this locality.

After the middle of May, in the north central states at least, Evergreens are starting to make their new season's growth. When in this new, soft growth, they easily heat or burn when closely packed in boxes and shipped. Furthermore, it is impossible to handle a tree in this condition without breaking off some of the new buds and thereby hindering the growth of that branch for the season. Also, in disturbing a tree at this season, the normal growth is interfered with, and the shock of cutting the roots when the tree is demanding the most of its roots in the way of moisture and nourishment is a great handicap to the tree.

Spring has always been the natural time for transplanting. At that time of the year our thoughts turn to the out-of-doors, and there is more interest in planting then than at other times during the year.

Fall Planting Season

On the other hand, fall planting has many fine advantages. More and more people are taking advantage of the long fall season to transplant and to re-arrange their grounds. In the fall, the planting season usually opens about the middle of September and continues until the ground freezes, usually about December 1st. Fall-planted trees should be planted during late September or early October, for best results, and this is the season which we recommend. Fall-planted trees make some new root growth before winter. Then, of course, they are in the ground and ready to grow with the first beginning of spring.

After all, it is not so much a matter of when to plant, as the manner in which the planting is done, and the conditions under which the planting is made. A few rules for transplanting, which are given elsewhere in this book, are more important than the exact time for doing the work. It is a good plan, however, to keep the planting within the periods recommended above.

THE TWO TRANSPLANTING SEASONS

For planters living in the north central states, the spring planting season usually does not begin before the last week in March, as the ground is not thawed out and in workable condition until then. By the middle of May, Evergreens are usually too far advanced in growth for transplanting.

The fall season in the north central states usually begins about the middle of September, as soon as there have been sufficient fall rains to allow digging trees. Planting must stop by the middle of November, sometimes before, as the ground is usually frozen by that time.

Chapter XIX

Soil Requirements for Evergreens

BETWEEN the lack of information and the misinformation on the subject of soil for Evergreens, there seems to be a need for a few simple suggestions.

People have their own views on classifying soil. To many people, soil is either "good or poor." Others divide it into lime or acid soil. Some planters are content to simply refer to soil as red, brown, or black. These terms mean but little, of course, in determining whether soil is favorable for the growth of Evergreen trees.

Our first approach to this problem of soil leads us to the native haunts of Evergreens. What do we find? In the swamps we will find the Arborvitae, the Bald Cypress, the Black Spruce and the Larch. We must not conclude that these trees will, therefore, grow only on damp ground. Rather they grow *in spite of* the dampness.

Consider the White Pine. We find it on high ground, on stony hillsides. But it also grows along the moist river bottoms. In fact nature seems to show a disregard for soil. High land, low land, gravel, sand, clay and rich, black soil all produce Evergreens in the wild state.

These observations do not, therefore, answer the question. They do, however, indicate that other conditions beside soil influence tree growth. They also indicate that some soils are better for tree growth than others.

In general we may conclude that a loose, sandy loam, well-drained, is the ideal soil for most Evergreens. While we cannot undertake to change our soil to any extent, we can avoid certain conditions and correct some faults.

Subsoil which has been taken out in excavating basements, or soil which is mixed with the trash of building operations, and which is frequently found around new homes, should be dug out and good soil brought in.

A very heavy, stiff, clay soil should be mixed with sand or peat moss to make it more porous to permit the roots to easily penetrate it.

Except in the case of a very few species as mentioned above, Evergreens will not grow when the ground is wet, soggy, or poorly drained. If poor drainage exists, the soil should be dug out several feet deep and some coarse material filled in so that water will not stand around the roots.

Do not expect Evergreens to do well in soil that has been packed hard and not cultivated for many years. Such soil must be replaced.

Where soil is very shallow, with rock close to the surface, there is not much opportunity for Evergreens to grow.

Often we mistake a condition of deep shade, or planting made too close to buildings, or trees too crowded, for a fault of soil. Even in good soil, Evergreens cannot overcome these handicaps. Application of fertilizer and the use of peat moss will help materially in overcoming the bad effects of a poor planting site and an unfavorable condition of soil.

It is not necessary that we become soil-technologists in order to succeed with our trees. In instances where trees are planted to insure their long life as specimens over a long period of years, some attention to soil conditions will prove a great benefit.

On the other hand, in the planting of trees around the home grounds for ornamental use, soil conditions need not concern planters to any extent, as such plantings are intended for only a few years use, with no thought in view of establishing trees which will endure for generations.

Elsewhere in this book are suggestions for selection of certain Evergreens for special conditions of soil.

These remarks on soil refer to the conifers, or narrow-leaved Evergreens. Certain of the so-called broad-leaved Evergreens, such as Rhododendrons, Azaleas, etc., prefer an acid soil. For this reason they do not thrive in northern Illinois, or in other localities where there is an abundance of lime in the soil.

About 12 years ago, children at play in a New England pasture, carried to the summit of a large granite rock a small plant of Redcedar and without giving attention to a single one of the rules that are usually observed in transplanting Conifers, crowded its roots into a crevice. A little earth was laboriously supplied. The Juniper grew on, year after year. It is now in perfect health and ten feet high.

How, may we ask, did the Juniper, seventeen feet above the ground on the top of a rock, exposed to the full heat of the sun in a time of excessive and abnormal drought, obtain the needed moisture for its survival? Rocks are comparable to saturated sponges, which soaked with water are reservoirs of coolness and moisture that nature uses. A rock mass absorbs moisture and gives it off to the atmosphere and to the roots of plants. Photograph and text kindly furnished by the Arnold Arboretum, Jamaica Plain, Mass.

CHAPTER XX

Peat Moss—What It Is and Does

PEAT moss has only recently become extensively used in the United States, although European gardeners have long known of its many benefits. "Peat" is classified according to the origin of its composition. Peat moss is peat formed through the partial decay of various mosses. It might be better named moss peat. It is light brown in color and odorless.

Other forms of peat composed of reeds, grasses, or decayed vegetable matter are totally different products. Peat is found in swamps or bogs, to a considerable depth, throughout the world, but the types found in Germany, Sweden and Holland are by far the most valuable and useful. It is cut out in blocks, thoroughly dried, and then ground or granulated. There are different degrees of fineness for various purposes. Peat moss suitable for use with Evergreens is commercially known as Horticultural Peat Moss.

HIGHLY ABSORBENT

It is free from fungus and weed seeds, highly absorbent, holding water like minute sponges, and is useful in many ways to the gardener, for lawns, gardens, etc. Our discussion of peat moss is only with reference to its value in planting and in mulching Evergreens. It is available in bales, tightly compressed, which make twenty to twenty-two bushels of moss when opened.

A bale of tightly-compressed peat moss will make over twenty bushels when broken up and made ready for application. Illustration courtesy of Atkins & Durbrow.

Good peat moss will hold seven times its own weight in water, in contrast to good garden soil which will absorb only one-half its own dry weight in moisture, and sand which will take up only one-fifth of its weight in moisture. This peat moss is the greatest reservoir known for retaining moisture in the soil, when it is mixed into the soil. In planting Evergreens, we recommend that peat moss be mixed with soil at the rate of one-fourth peat moss and three-fourths soil.

Improves Soil

It breaks up, and renders more friable, heavy and clay soils. It binds and gives more body to loose, sandy soil. It also acts as a reservoir for plant food, applied in the form of commercial fertilizer.

Promotes Root Growth

The greatest benefit of peat moss is in promoting root growth. Experiments have clearly shown that fine, fibrous roots develop in one-third of the time and in greater number when peat moss is mixed with the soil. It can safely be said that the period of experimenting is over. Peat moss is a very definite boon to gardening, and it should be used freely to make trees grow quicker and better.

For Mulching

Peat is also freely used as a summer mulch on the surface of the soil. In this way it keeps the ground moist, keeps down weeds, saves cultivation, and gives a neat, attractive finish to plantings. Used in winter, it helps to maintain a more even temperature and reduces the extremes of freezing and thawing.

Do not overlook peat moss in your other gardening activities for bulbs, trees, shrubs and lawns.

One thing you must remember when using peat moss as a summer mulch—when watering the garden spray the top well and soak the ground underneath the mulch. If you do this the length of the interval between waterings may be doubled and often trebled.

"Gardening with Peat Moss," by F. F. Rockwell, and published by Atkins & Durbrow, Inc., New York, is an excellent little book thoroughly covering the subject of Peat Moss.

Break the peat moss up fine and spread it out with a rake.
Illustration courtesy of Atkins & Durbrow.

CHAPTER XXI

Fertilizers for Evergreens

THE list of materials recognized by the Association of Official Agricultural Chemists as fertilizer materials, is no less than two hundred. These materials include by-products of stock yards and sewage disposal plants, residue of many various manufacturing processes, other waste products, natural manures, and chemical compounds. Unless one is a user of fertilizers in large quantity, or has some particular fertilizer available locally at a great saving in cost, it is much simpler to use a ready-mixed chemical fertilizer especially prepared and recommended for some particular purpose. Fertilizer *is not all suited* to the same purpose.

Almost all fertilizers, regardless of origin or chemical analysis, are of value to Evergreens only in so far as they contain and make easily available the following materials: nitrogen, phosphoric acid, and potash. Analysis of fertilizer is always stated in this order. Thus, a 10-8-6 analysis means 10% nitrogen, 8% phosphoric acid and 6% potash.

After long experiment with various fertilizers, a product known as Hill Evergreen Tree Food has been developed and is available to planters. This is a special formula containing 10-8-6, which has been found, through extensive experiment, to produce best results with Evergreens. Not only will the growth and the general health of the tree be benefited, but the color will be more pronounced when trees are properly fed using this food.

Directions for application: Use one-half pound per foot in height of tree. Example:

> 2-foot trees, 1 pound fertilizer.
> 3-foot trees, 1½ pounds.
> 4-foot trees, 2 pounds.
> Larger trees in proportion.

Apply *after* the tree is planted. Dig a shallow trench around the stem of the tree near the edge of the spread of the branches, and sprinkle in fertilizer in the above proportion and cover with soil. The rain or watering will carry the fertilizer down to the roots.

For established trees, make one application in April and another in July or in August.

Old plantings of large Evergreens which are not in robust condition can also be greatly benefited. In such cases, dig small holes if possible with an auger, 18 inches or more deep, about every two feet, extending entirely around the tree and out well to the edge of the spread of the branches. In each hole place a small handful of fertilizer, and replace the dirt and sod.

Do not place fertilizer in the hole during planting, or in direct contact with the roots. Do not use more than the amount specified nor make application more than twice each year.

Fertilizer applied to Evergreens indiscriminately, with no thought of its physical properties or its strength, is the cause of many a disappointing failure of the trees.

The abundant use of fertilizer is not the panacea for all ills of Evergreens, nor will its use overcome an unfavorable planting location, a lack of watering, or neglect of cultivation. These things are all more important than the fine points of chemistry concerning the value of certain materials used as fertilizers.

It is possible to "kill Evergreens with kindness." One planter's experiences could be related for the benefit of other planters. His entire planting of Evergreens died after he had given them the "very best of care." First, he dug out all the soil where his planting was put in, and filled in with black dirt secured from a nearby greenhouse. This was very rich soil to begin with. Then he mixed bone meal with it. Then he gave a generous application of a well known commercial fertilizer. It was too rich a diet and his trees could not survive it. If this planter had merely used his greenhouse dirt and no fertilizer, or used his regular soil with a light treatment of plant food of some kind, his trees would have been alive and healthy.

Natural Manure

The French word "manure" originally meant to till or work the soil, and later included the addition of materials to enrich the soil. In America we usually use the word to designate the excreta of animals, as it is usually available, mixed with straw or bedding litter. Manure is not readily available in many localities and even then is not easy to store and handle. However, it still remains an important fertilizer material when properly treated. Fresh stable manure is not suitable for use on Evergreens. Only after it has been piled up for two or three years and composted, is it safe to mix with the soil in a limited way in planting Evergreens.

Liquid Manure

After immersing a bag of manure in a barrel of water for several days, the liquid may be drawn off and applied to Evergreens, especially those in weakened condition.

Other Common Fertilizers

Among the more common fertilizers we will mention a few briefly.

Bone meal, which is strong in phosphorus, is slow-acting and remains in the soil a long time before it benefits the trees. It is a one-sided ration only.

Dried blood is valuable for its nitrogen content (about twelve per cent), which is quickly available to plants. It is a good fertilizer material.

Lime, whether in the form of slaked lime or ground limestone, also adds to soil fertility by neutralizing acid compounds, and promoting the formation of nitrates. It also helps to make other plant foods in the soil more available. Lime should be applied only to soils in which it is deficient, and then, as a rule, in compost.

No attempt is made here to offer comments on the many commercial tree foods which have been put on the market in recent years. They should be used strictly according to the recommendations of the manufacturer.

Fertilizing in the Nursery

Large amounts of potash, phosphorus, nitrogen, and other chemical elements are taken yearly from the soil by growing nursery stock. Nursery stock can be successfully grown for a period of several years on exceptionally good soils without manuring, but sooner or later the application of fertilizer becomes necessary.

As the nursery stock leaves nothing on the ground to decay and form humus, soiling crops and stable manure are usually preferable to concentrated or commercial fertilizers when used alone.

Cover Crops as Fertilizers

A great variety of fertilizer plants are used. Leguminous crops, such as cowpeas, field peas, soy beans, and lupines are usually best for this purpose because of their importance in increasing the supply of nitrogen. Buckwheat and rye are often useful where nitrogen is supplied in other forms, because of the large amount of organic matter produced in a comparatively short time and the volume of humus that results from their decay. The crop is plowed under while still green. It is then covered with a heavy dressing of well-rotted farm manure at the rate of ten to fifty tons per acre.

Farm manures are the most useful fertilizers for general purposes that can be used in nursery practice, either alone or in combination with other materials composted with them. This is particularly true whenever they can be obtained at reasonable cost. Not only are they rich in plant food, but their bulk makes them of superior value in improving the physical condition of the soil. Cow manure is better than horse manure. Much less time is required for its decomposition. Farm manures in the fresh state should be used only when applied to farm crops or soiling crops in rotation with nursery crops. Fresh manures should be rotted either out of doors in piles, known as compost heaps, or under cover, where loss from leaching is prevented.

CHAPTER XXII

How and When to Water Evergreens

EVERGREENS in the native forests receive no water except that which rains provide. When we see these towering specimens, and how they maintain their vigor without artificial watering, we may conclude that all Evergreens, therefore, will get along without watering. But when we study the forest condition, we see that the earth is covered to a considerable depth with rich, cool, moist, humus soil, the result of centuries of decaying vegetable matter. This acts as a blanket to hold moisture in the soil. We must also recognize that the roots of forest trees reach deeply into the ground, down to the permanent water level, which is normally found at various depths beneath the surface, and which rarely dries out. In periods of long and severe drought, even forest trees suffer and sometimes die from water-starvation.

Evergreens in city and suburban-plantings are faced with an entirely different set of conditions. There is no natural mulch to hold the moisture. The ground dries out easily, and, until the trees reach considerable size, their roots do not penetrate deeply into the soil. They must depend on artificial watering to provide sufficient moisture. Evaporation is continually going on through the leaves of Evergreens, more extensively in summer, but to some extent at all times. The moisture is taken up by the roots. When there is no moisture in the soil, the leaves or needles dry out, turn brown, and fall off. Then the tree dies.

For the first two years at least, Evergreens need watering and under adverse circumstances of soil or location, they may need occasional watering during the entire life of the tree.

There is no rule to lay down that will cover every planting condition. Bear in mind that the roots must be kept moist, but not constantly wet. It is better to water thoroughly at less frequent intervals than to do it daily. Many people make the mistake of sprinkling the top of the soil each day. Such a practice does more harm than good. It encourages the roots to grow upward, close to the surface to seek moisture. Then they are more than ever less able to withstand drought.

It is better to remove the nozzle from the hose and allow a small stream of water to soak into the ground until the soil will not absorb any more water. This may take several hours. Then see that a mulch of loose soil or peat moss is spread around the tree to check the rapid evaporation. Even during dry weather, one such watering at intervals of ten days or two weeks is sufficient.

There is no doubt that rain water is better, when available, but hydrant water, unless it is highly charged with minerals, will do no harm. Rainfall is apt to be ample during the early spring months, as well as in the fall. It is during July, August, and September that watering is most needed. Newly-planted trees, of course, need water when planted and then again a few days afterward.

Do not water the tops of Evergreens when the sun is shining, but an occasional, thorough washing of the tops in the evening removes the dust and helps the tree to perform its normal functions.

In localities where there is much oil, soot, or other impurities in the air, an annual washing of the foliage is necessary. When the needles are heavily coated in this way, the rays of the sun cannot perform the necessary reaction in the needles of the tree and the tree becomes weak and unhealthy.

This greasy coating cannot be removed by water. Recently a new product has been developed called "Calgon," which dissolves this greasy covering and does no harm to the tree. It is applied in a solution of water and is then rinsed off with a hose.

Where there is too much sulphur or other gases in the air, the successful raising of Evergreens is simply out of the question.

In conclusion it may be said that more trees die from lack of water than any other cause. Let your watering program be governed by common sense. It is better to overdo it than to neglect it altogether.

On this rock in Lake Superior a Pine tree has been growing for nearly forty years. How it was planted we cannot say; perhaps birds deposited the seed, or some person transplanted it there just to see if it would grow.

While such a location might seem to defy the rules for watering, actually this peculiar situation has its merits. It is a well-known fact that rocks are great conductors of moisture, and as this rock sets constantly in water, an ample supply of moisture no doubt reaches the roots by capillary attraction.

Chapter XXIII

Winter Care of Evergreens

LATE in the fall, after the ground has frozen, it is a good plan to provide a mulch of dry leaves, hay, or well-rotted stable manure around each tree. This mulch could be ten inches to a foot deep, and extend out well beyond the natural spread of the roots. This treatment is especially beneficial when planting has been done during the fall months.

Weight it down with dirt, light slats or boards to prevent the wind from blowing it off during winter. A mulch of this kind holds the frost in check, prevents continued thawing and freezing, and keeps the wind from swaying the trees so that the soil does not become loosened and there is little possibility of an air pocket forming about the stem and drying out the roots. If well-rotted straw, hay, or stable litter has been used, spade in well around the base of the tree in spring. Any mulch that is of no value as fertilizer, should be removed in early spring as soon as frost is out of the ground and cultivation commenced.

Protection to Tops

Most damage to tender Evergreens comes not from severe cold, but from the sudden changes of temperature, the sweeping winds, and the late winter sun. Particularly when exposed to the southern sun in February and March, some Evergreens will suffer a browning or burning of the needles. This may be prevented by some such device as the one illustrated. A piece of burlap erected on stakes will give all the protection necessary. Do not make these enclosures too small, or so tight that the air cannot circulate freely, or so that the tree will start to bud out earlier than it should.

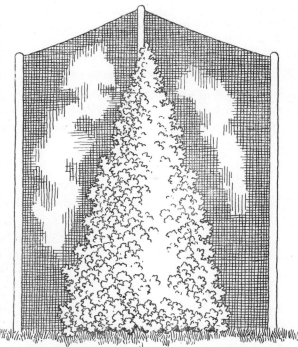

This protection will also be beneficial where trees are in exposed locations.

Ice and Snow Damage

Since Evergreens retain their leaves in winter, they easily catch the snow and ice. During heavy ice and sleet storms branches may need to be supported to prevent damage.

What is Meant by "Hardy"

Such terms, which are often used to describe Evergreens, are of little meaning in themselves. It is only when applied to a tree in a specific locality or latitude that these terms may be employed with any degree of accuracy.

For example, a tree said to be hardy in New Orleans, should be able to withstand the normal extremes of winter there. There are rare occasions when temperatures drop suddenly, and trees suffer badly or are killed outright, but these are not normal conditions. The same tree might prove half-hardy in Memphis. That is, it might survive for a time in a favorable location during a cycle of mild winters. In Chicago this tree would be too tender for the rigors of winter and therefore be considered not hardy. Some other variety of Evergreen might thrive in Chicago, be half-hardy in Duluth, and too tender in Winnipeg.

The sea, the ocean currents, the mountains, the plains, and the Great Lakes all have an influence on climate, and in turn on plant life. For example, it is well known that some parts of the state of Michigan, which is almost surrounded by the Great Lakes, can grow certain kinds of trees which are not hardy a few hundred miles south.

A tree which fails to grow in an exposed windswept plain in Nebraska, might do well in the protection of a forest of trees in Minnesota.

Soil and rainfall also have some influence on hardiness. In localities where fall rains keep trees growing until late in the fall, and then the temperature drops suddenly, more tender trees may suffer. On the other hand, where the growth is fully hardened up with the coming of winter, the same tree might live year after year.

The Arnold Arboretum in Boston is slightly farther north than Chicago, but many kinds of Evergreens grow in Boston which are failures in northern Illinois.

Humidity and snowfall also influence the behavior of Evergreens.

There is often a great difference in the hardiness of certain strains of the same tree. Where a tree in its native range extends, for example, all the way from New Mexico to Montana, it naturally makes a great difference in the hardiness of the trees grown from seed from the two extremes of latitude.

Evergreens may also be acclimated to a locality by degrees. By taking cuttings or grafts from a particular tree which has existed for some years considerably north of its normal latitude, new trees may be grown which will often reproduce the same exceptional hardiness of their parent.

Thus it may be seen that the term "Hardy Evergreen" is after all a term of questionable meaning. Planters, therefore, must rely somewhat on the nurseryman to furnish types of Evergreens suitable for their climate. Only one precaution might be given. It may be better, when possible, to obtain Evergreens from a supplier whose location is not in too great contrast to your own.

Cultivation

Cultivation is one of the most important points to remember in the culture of Evergreens. Planters are sometimes negligent in cultivation and fail to do anything about it until their trees start to show signs of neglect. It is a good plan to start cultivation immediately after planting. Keep the ground in a cultivated state around newly planted trees. This conserves the moisture in the ground and prevents evaporation, keeps the grass and weeds from interfering with the growth, and improves the appearance of your planting wonderfully. Cultivation is especially important where the ground is naturally hard and easily dried out. The drier the season, the greater the necessity for cultivation.

The cultivation of an area around old trees will help unusually in prolonging their life and keeping them vigorous and healthy.

Most old trees suffer from starvation and dryness due to the hard, packed ground around them.

The "dust-mulch" is especially necessary with Evergreens. By "dust-mulch" is meant a layer of loose earth, three or four inches deep, made by weekly stirring of the soil with a hoe all through the summer months, from the middle of May to the first of September. This prevents baking and cracking of the soil and the escape of moisture.

The Maintenance of a cultivated area, equal to the spread of branches, around Evergreens keeps out grass and weeds and helps to retain moisture.

CHAPTER XXIV

How to Prune Evergreens

T HE art of pruning Evergreens is not an easy subject to explain; neither is it one on which all gardeners agree.

During recent years, Evergreens have been used extensively in foundation plantings and other small areas around the grounds, and the need for frequent pruning has therefore developed.

Fig. 1. Pruning overdone.

To paraphrase an old maxim, we might say "spare the knife and spoil the tree." But we must not take this too literally. Many plantings of Evergreens have been ruined by someone with a mania for trimming. See figure 1. Every tree, regardless of its natural habit, has been trimmed after the same pattern. This creates an artificial and monotonous appearance and ruins the beauty of the tree as nature intended it to grow.

In contrast to this type of pruning, we see plantings which have been entirely neglected. See figure 2. These sometimes become "leggy," irregular, weak, and thinned in appearance, and if allowed to go without attention, soon fail entirely to fill the place in the planting for which they were intended. Between these two extremes, there is a reasonable middle course.

Rules for pruning Evergreens are dangerous unless tempered with the judgment of him who

Fig. 2. Pruning neglected.

is doing the pruning. This fact is apparent when we realize that no two trees are alike. Each plant has individual characteristics. Some are by nature conical; some, columnar; some, globular, and some, prostrate. Suggestions cannot, therefore, be definite, iron-clad rules to be followed without variation.

It is not good practice to prune Evergreens into shapes too far removed from their natural habit. For example, do not try to make a Norway Spruce into a ball shape, nor train an Irish Juniper into a broad pyramid. We must consider the art of pruning, not as a creative operation, but as a corrective one. Unusual pruning, such as that illustrated in figure 3, shows what may be accomplished by careful and persistent efforts. The design of such grotesque exhibits is limited only by the imagination of the pruner. Such examples of the pruner's art, if it may be so called, have a place as curiosities, but are of course, beyond the purpose of normal pruning operations.

The Purpose of Pruning

Let us first consider the purpose of pruning. We prune Evergreens for any of several reasons enumerated below:

To keep the tree within certain limits of size.

To remove any diseased or injured part of the tree.

To shape the tree into some special form.

To invigorate a weak tree.

Fig. 3. A curious example of pruning near Hanover, Germany, ninety years old.

Pruning Should Begin in the Nursery

Many years of neglect in pruning cannot be suddenly corrected by one pruning. It is better to begin when the tree is small and give a little attention each year.

In a well-conducted Evergreen nursery, the matter of early pruning receives careful attention, not as a routine piece of work, but with due regard to the characteristics of the particular species and variety being grown.

No pruning of the top of Evergreens is done while the trees are in seed beds, or in the greenhouse. Neither is it necessary, except in rare instances, to do any pruning during the period that the trees are in transplant beds. The first pruning begins at the time the trees are planted out into rows in the nursery.

The method of pruning is quite different for the various families of Evergreens. Some Evergreens have fine, soft foliage and numerous, small, flexible branchlets. Other families have stiff branches with a well defined formation of the branching habit of the tree. We will try to explain and illustrate the various steps followed in the pruning of some of the more common kinds of Evergreens.

First Steps in Pruning Junipers

When Juniper grafts are taken from the greenhouse and are planted out into field rows in the nursery, they are immediately staked. That is, the stem of the tree is tied to a stiff wire stake, with at least two ties of raffia, or soft string, as shown in figure 5.

It is necessary to do this because the stem, or trunk, of a Juniper is not stiff enough, when small, to hold the tree straight and upright. The low-growing and spreading Junipers, and even the creeping Junipers, are also staked up for the first few years, in order to keep the stem of the tree from resting flat on the ground. This early method of staking the low-growing forms greatly improves the future growth of such trees.

By the end of the summer, if there has been a normal growing season, the trees are ready for the first light pruning. The first pruning is illustrated in

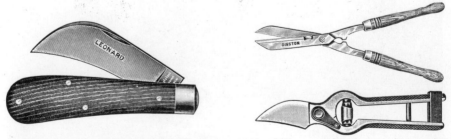

Fig. 4. Three tools make up the pruner's equipment: a pruning knife, a pruning shears, and a two-handled hedge shears. Pruning shears should be kept sharp and clean. Illustration courtesy of Tool Division. A. M. Leonard and Son.

figure 6. The tops are cut back a little and any side branches that are growing too fast are also cut back. This is done with a sharp pruning-knife with an upward, freehand movement. This treatment is very modestly given the first season. Some individual trees need a good deal of trimming; some, perhaps, none at all. Some varieties require much more pruning than others. The amount of trimming necessary for any tree will become obvious after a little practice. You can rarely hurt the tree by too much pruning. Spreading and creeping types of Junipers are also pruned to give greater strength to the branches.

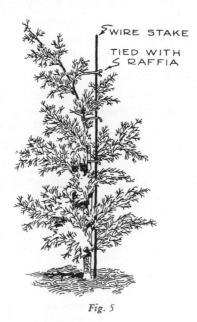

During the fall months and the following spring, the branches will grow out again, with more inner branches and smaller branchlets. See figure 7. The branches should be cut back again at the end of the second summer, and the same treatment should be continued each year during the growth of the tree. It is not always necessary or wise to prune Junipers every summer. Sometimes, with slower growers, or during a dry season when there has been but little growth, the trees can be left until the summer of the next year.

Fig. 5

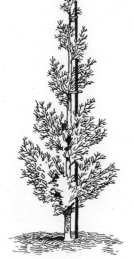

Fig. 6

Fig. 7

Figure 8 shows a Juniper about ten years old and five feet tall in the nursery. It has been transplanted four times and has had six prunings. When the customer receives such a tree, it only needs the ends of the branches and the top trimmed a little each summer to keep it compact and shapely. The pruning can be done anytime during late spring and the early part of the summer, either with a pruning knife or shears.

By contrast, figure 9 makes a sorry spectacle. Its development is no exaggeration of what may be expected of certain varieties of Junipers left entirely untouched. Other Junipers make a more natural, stiff trunk, but will be very thin and open if trimming is neglected.

The variety of Evergreen represented in these sketches is the Silver Redcedar (*Juniperus virginiana glauca*). Almost exactly the same procedure is followed with all Junipers, except for the differences in the severity of pruning in different growers, and the natural habit of the tree. Some varieties which are of extremely narrow habit are trimmed to accentuate that habit. A broad-growing tree is trimmed so as to develop a broad growth. Likewise a ball-shaped tree is trimmed ball-shaped; a spreading Juniper is kept low, etc. The time of pruning and the

Fig. 8   Fig. 9

frequency of pruning are the same, however, regardless of the individual characteristics of the particular variety.

The suggestions as outlined for Junipers, apply to all families of Evergreens which have numerous small buds and whose branches do not grow in definite layers or whorls, such as Arborvitaes, Yews, Hemlocks, Cypress, and Chamaecyparis. The branches of the Evergreens of these families can be pruned without much regard to the terminal of a branch. In other families of Evergreens, which make strong, terminal buds, the pruning can be done as explained in the next section.

How to Prune Pines, Firs, Spruces, Etc.

The pruning of Pines, Firs, and Spruces follows a different method, in keeping with the character of the branching habits of the trees. As in the case of Junipers previously discussed, the pruning should begin early in the life of

Fig. 10. A beautiful garden in Peekskill, New York. The formality of design requires formal, trimmed, specimens of Evergreens. An instance where severe and skillful trimming must be exercised.

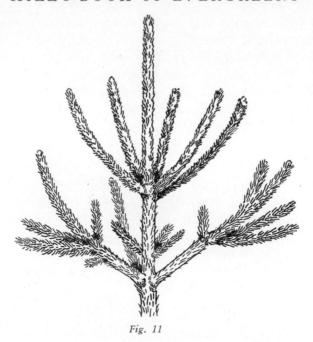

Fig. 11

the tree. Trees of this type grow in whorls or layers of branches as illustrated in figure 11.

The pruning of this group of Evergreens is confined largely to correcting defects and in cutting back to make the tree more compact and dense in growth.

Sometimes injuries such as late frosts will kill the side buds, but perhaps leave the top or terminal bud uninjured. All of the energy of the tree may then go into the growth of the top, producing an abnormal growth; or the

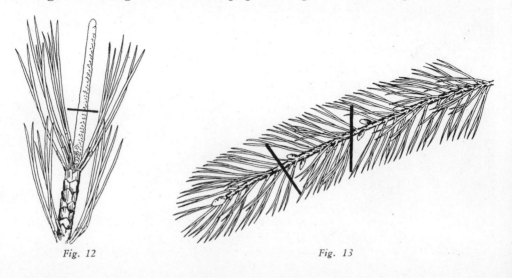

Fig. 12   *Fig. 13*

condition may be reversed, with injury to the top bud and abnormal growth of some side branches. If this top growth is not cut back, there may be an interval of two or three feet of bare trunk. By cutting back this abnormal growth, the shape of the tree will be normal in following years.

Figure 12 shows the normal, extended bud of a Pine just before the needles develop. By cutting off two-thirds or more of this new bud, the tree will make but a short growth and the following year will throw out more side branchlets. If a thick, close growth is wanted, this trimming of the buds each spring will be a great help. In case some one branch grows much too fast, the entire bud may be pinched out or broken off. That branch will, therefore, not grow at all, and the weaker branches as a result will become stronger.

If for some reason it becomes necessary to cut into the old wood, the branch should be cut near an axillary bud. That is, a bud which is developing to produce foliage the following year, as shown in figure 13.

The pruning of new buds must, of course, take place at the time when the new buds are forming. This period varies in different latitudes. In the vicinity of northern Illinois, late May or early June is the proper time.

REPAIRING A LOST OR DAMAGED LEADER

Evergreens which grow with a single main stem or trunk are sometimes injured through breaking the top or leader. This damage is more apt to be found among the Spruces, Firs, Pines and trees which make a stiff straight stem. The loss of the leader need not be a permanent injury.

First, select one of the side branches near the top of the tree which can easily be trained upward to start a new leader. This side branch must be tied in place and fastened to a wooden or wire stake with soft cord. After a year or two in this position, the defect in the appearance of the tree is scarcely noticeable. See figures 14 and 15.

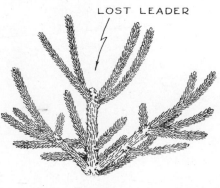

Fig. 14

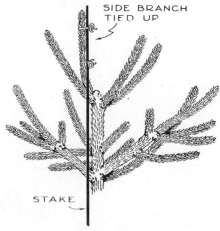

Fig. 15

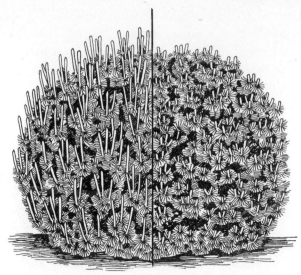

Fig. 16

The pruning of Mugho Pine might well deserve a special paragraph of explanation. Much depends upon first obtaining the true, dwarf, many-stemmed variety. A wide variation exists in the native types of Mugho Pine. The area of distribution takes in the greater part of the mountain ranges of central and southern Europe, existing at altitudes up to 8,000 feet. Many localities where seed is easily accessible produce either a type of tree with a single stem or a loose, open growth not attractive in cultivation.

In order to maintain trees in a compact growth, the pruning should be done annually in late May or early June (depending, according to locality, upon when the buds have reached their greatest maturity before opening into leaves). Normally, each branch will make a shoot or candle-like growth of two inches to five or six inches long. Two-thirds or more of this growth should be cut off with a knife or pruning-shears, as illustrated in figure 16. Mugho Pines which are neglected will grow with a loose habit as shown in figure 17.

Fig. 17

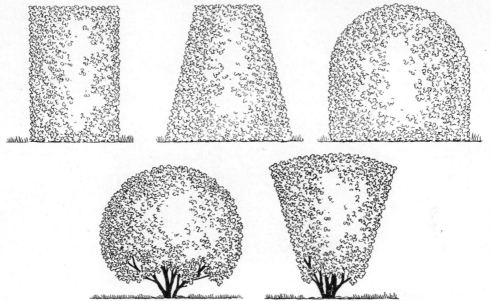

Fig. 18. *Trim so that the base of the hedge is as wide or wider than the top. Sunlight then reaches the bottom and keeps the hedge thrifty and healthy. Avoid trimming in shapes as shown in the two bottom figures.*

SUGGESTIONS FOR PRUNING EVERGREEN HEDGES

Evergreen hedges can be pruned at once after planting, but the first trimming should not be too severe. Remove any straggling or irregular branches and bring the individual trees into as nearly the same size as possible. The permanent shaping of the hedge will require a watchful eye and a careful hand. The necessary time to develop a solid wall will be four to five years. Trim once a year, either in the spring before the growth starts, or in summer after the growth has been made.

Figure 18 shows suggestions for the pruning of the hedge and what to avoid in the contour.

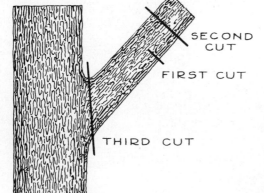

SECOND CUT

FIRST CUT

THIRD CUT

Fig. 19

REMOVING LARGE LIMBS

When occasion requires removal of large branches in old trees, the work can be done with a saw. If performed in the manner illustrated, a branch can be cut without tearing the bark or splitting the wood. Such pruning can be done at any time of the year.

The Japanese Art of "Dwarfing" Evergreens

It may be interesting to give some brief mention under the heading of "Pruning" to the unique practice of producing gnarled and twisted miniature Evergreens in pots. This is a specialized exhibition of horticultural skill as practiced by the Japanese, a race with whom gardening is a most highly developed art. The trees were formerly imported extensively from Japan for table and interior decoration, and they would doubtless still be in demand if quarantine laws would permit their importation at present.

The charm of these trees lies in the perfection with which every part of the tree is developed in true proportion. They are, in fact, miniature trees, so perfectly done that if removed from their background, they cannot be distinguished from life-size trees.

Various legends exist in Japan as to the origin of the practice of growing these trees. A popular myth relates the story of an Emperor of Japan who lived 2500 years ago, who was without an heir. A son was finally presented to him, but with the odd provision that the boy would retain the stature of a new born child until he was 15 years old. The Emperor constructed a miniature house with everything in reduced proportion, which, of course, also called for dwarf trees. Thus, was the beginning of the practice of growing these miniature specimens of trees, a custom which is now one of the most extensive hobbies of many Japanese.

Illustration courtesy of Yokohama Nursery Co., Yokohama, Japan.

Doubtless, the density of population in Japan and the extensive loss of the forests has instilled a love of trees which finds expression in the creation of the little, potted trees. The high regard in which these trees are held is no doubt due in some measure to the expression for art and beauty which their development provide.

There is a widespread belief that these little trees are hundreds of years old. Some few specimens no doubt are of great age, and some are very valuable. True it is, that no other race of gardeners has been able to muster the skill required to develop the impression of age and dignity that the Japanese trees possess. The trees which we see photographed are, of course, the choice specimens. Every effort at dwarfing is not so skillfully accomplished. The selection of suitable varieties is, therefore, a part of the secret. Cypress and Pines, Arborvitae and Cedars are all used. Delicate slits are sometimes made in the bark which permits twisting the stem in curious shapes. Wire or twine is used to tie a twisted or gnarled branch in place until it grows a permanent deformity. Some leaves and branchlets are removed and others bent and formed to give an air of great age. So cleverly is this done that a lifetime in appearance can be added in a few seasons' growth.

Prof. Albert A. Hansen wrote in the *Country Gentleman* several years ago: "The easiest manner in which to produce a dwarf tree is to prune the root system of a young seedling as heavily as the plant will endure and still look healthy. Each time the plant is repotted the roots should be pruned severely. The effect will be a stunting of the growth, which will be aided by lightly cutting back the tips of the branches, thereby securing greater ramification in the foliage.

"In the Orient youthful dwarfs are made to assume the appearance of great age by covering the tree with sirup and allowing ants to attack. They not only eat the sirup, but devour part of the sweetened bark, giving the plant an aged and weather-beaten appearance."

Some elaborate landscapes are occasionally built in miniature around some venerable-looking tree.

Illustrations courtesy of Yokohama Nursery Co., Yokohama, Japan.

Chapter XXV

Weights - Packing and Shipping Information

SOME idea of the weight of Evergreens and how they are packed and shipped will be helpful to anyone who expects to secure Evergreens from a distance. When purchased from a local nursery, these details are of no particular interest to the planter, as the trees may be delivered to your door by truck.

Seedlings, cuttings, grafts, and small transplanted Evergreens, dug without earth on the roots, are generally packed in ventilated wooden boxes. The roots are packed in spagnum moss to keep them moist. The trees are tied in bundles and securely cleated to avoid any possibility of becoming loose in the box. Except when purchased in large quantities, such shipments are generally sent by express. At the present time Evergreens take the second class express rate, which is a saving of approximately twenty-five per cent over the first class rate. Large shipments of this class of stock are frequently sent by freight where considerable weight is involved. The ratio between freight and express rates is not the same to all points. However, the average less carload freight rates are approximately fifty per cent of the express rates. Small shipments weighing up to twenty pounds may be sent by parcel post, packed in cardboard boxes, or in parcels wrapped with waterproof paper.

When properly packed, small trees may be shipped a long distance with perfect safety, if handled during the proper season when the trees are dormant.

Weight of Small Evergreens

The following are actual weights taken from an average of many hundreds of shipments. The figures do not include the weight of packing material or boxes, which must be added to these figures.

The average weight of grafts is one-half pound each.

Packing

Seedlings per bundle of 50:

4 to 6 inches	1 to 2 pounds
6 to 8 inches	2 to 3 pounds
8 to 10 inches	3 to 5 pounds

Transplanted Evergreens 8 to 10 inches or smaller average five pounds per bundle of 25 trees.

Transplanted Evergreens 10 to 12 inches up to 12 to 18

124

inches average nine pounds per bundle of five trees.

In bulk, Evergreens of the above sizes will pack up somewhat as follows:

Quantity of trees	Class of Stock	Size of Trees	Size of Box	
			Length	Width
1,000	Seedlings	4 to 6 inches	2 feet	13x13 inches
1,000	Seedlings	6 to 8 inches	3 feet	13x13 inches
1,000	Transplants	6 to 8 inches	4 feet	15x15 inches
1,000	Transplants	8 to 10 inches	4 feet	19x19 inches
500	Transplants	10 to 12 inches	4 feet	26x26 inches
500	Transplants	12 to 18 inches	8 feet	26x26 inches

Note: These figures are *average* figures. Individual shipments may vary as much as 100 per cent, depending upon differences in the size of roots and tops.

Weight of Balled-and-Burlapped Evergreens

Evergreens are one of the most difficult commodities on which to give an accurate estimate of the weight. A great many factors enter into the calculations. Varieties differ in their root systems and, therefore, in the amount of dirt on the roots. Much depends upon the system of transplanting, as to whether a tree has many fine, fibrous roots confined to a small space, or whether the roots are coarse and spread out a great deal.

The time of year also has a bearing on the weight. In the fall the soil is apt to be more dry, and the weight, therefore, much less than during a rainy spring season. Some types of soil are naturally heavier than others.

In nearly all cases, except when shipped by truck, balled-and-burlapped Evergreens are packed in boxes and shipped by freight. When the bulk or weight is sufficient, shipments are made by freight in carloads, in which case no boxing is required, as the trees are packed directly into the cars. Provision is made to secure the trees properly to prevent shifting or breakage in transit. Shipments which are apt to encounter severe cold or heat in transit are shipped in refrigerator cars, otherwise they are moved in regular, closed freight cars, never in open cars.

The minimum weight which must be paid for when shipping in carloads is 12,000 pounds, except to certain localities where the minimum is higher. The average carload rate is about fifty per cent less than the less carload rate. Thus it will be seen that it is as cheap to ship as a carload, even though the weight is only 6,000 pounds. For example, the minimum cost of a carload of 12,000 pounds to a given point may be $60.00 figured at the rate of 50c per 100 pounds. The less carload rate to the same point is $1.00 per 100 pounds. Therefore, any weight of over 6,000 pounds is cheaper when shipped as a carload.

The approximate number of Evergreens which may be loaded in a 36-foot car is as follows:

Sizes	Number of Trees
1 to 3 feet—2 times transplanted B&B	1,000 to 2,000
1 to 2 feet—3 times transplanted B&B	500 to 750
2 to 5 feet—3 times transplanted B&B	300 to 600

Note: Twice transplanted trees are lighter grades, dug with small earth balls.

The average weight of the twice-transplanted, balled-and-burlapped items, based on the average of thirty-five individual varieties and sizes, is fifteen pounds.

The average weight of three-times-transplanted, balled-and-burlapped Evergreens, based on the average of several individual varieties and sizes, is as follows:

1 to 1½ feet—1½ to 2 feet average— 60 pounds
2 to 3   feet—3   to 4 feet average— 85 pounds
4 to 5   feet—5   to 6 feet average—115 pounds
6 to 7   feet—   average—200 pounds

Following are examples of the sized boxes needed for various quantities and sizes of balled-and-burlapped Evergreens:

Quantity of Trees	Class of Stock	Size of Trees	Size of Box Length	Width
50	xx B&B	1-1½ feet	4 foot	26x26 inches
10	xxx B&B	1-1½ feet	4 foot	26x26 inches
40	xx B&B	1½-2 feet	6 foot	26x26 inches
10	xxx B&B	1½-2 feet	6 foot	26x26 inches
15	xxx B&B	2-3 feet	8 foot	26x26 inches
10	xxx B&B	3-4 feet	8 foot	26x26 inches
10	xxx B&B	5-6 feet	10 foot	32x32 inches

Again we wish to mention that these figures are given only in an effort to furnish at least a rough idea of weights and costs of shipping. The many different circumstances which govern the weights may account for a considerable difference in the actual figures.

The weight of large Evergreens eight to ten feet and up, cannot be estimated in advance with any accuracy. The size of the earth ball depends on the nature of the root system of the tree; whether the roots are coarse or fine, and whether the tree has been frequently transplanted or not. Sometimes it is practical to make a smaller earth ball, following out the main roots with a spading fork so they will not be cut off, and securely wrapping these inside the burlap or canvas.

Chapter XXVI

How to Label Your Evergreens

ANY people who enjoy Evergreens and make a hobby of them take an interest in knowing their names and preserving their exact identity. The best type of label to use is sometimes a problem.

There are several common sorts of labels now in use—paper labels, wooden labels, zinc labels, copper labels and aluminum labels, as well as some patented kinds.

Paper Labels

No paper label is as permanent as one made of metal, but where the label is required for only a short period, a paper label in the form of a small, tough, manila tag will serve the purpose very well. Ink is of little use on paper labels, where they are to be used out doors; likewise, pencil marking is easily obliterated. A wax crayon will last longer than either ink or pencil.

Wooden Labels

A wooden label is often used where a large, easily read label is needed. They may be either painted or stenciled, and driven into the ground near the tree. If creosoted stakes are used and they are located where they will not be easily lost, or broken in cultivation, these labels can be preserved for several years. Black lettering on a white painted stake is easily read.

Zinc Labels

The simplest method of making zinc labels is to obtain sheet zinc cut to size, and allow it to be exposed to the weather several weeks in advance of making the labels, until thoroughly oxidized. On this oxidized surface the marks of an ordinary lead pencil will remain in good legible condition for several years. The oxidation, of course, can be aided by leaving the zinc in salt water for several days.

Zinc labels can also be made with especially prepared ink and a glass pen. Steel pens very quickly corrode. One good formula for writing fluid for zinc labels as recommended by the Missouri Botanical Garden is as follows: one dram of copper acetate, one dram ammonium chloride, one dram of lampblack, and ten drams of water.

Copper Labels

Copper labels are permanent, if the writing is done with some sharp instrument on a thin sheet of copper. Such labels should not be allowed to come in contact with the ground as they will easily corrode. They can be used permanently on a tree by fastening loosely on a branch, with a loose wire.

ALUMINUM LABELS

Where labeling is done on a large scale, as in nurseries or extensive grounds, an aluminum labeling machine is the most practical device. The aluminum comes in spools of various widths from one-half to two inches wide and is

fed through the machine, so that labels may be any length desired. The names are embossed by pressure on a hand lever. These labels may be either hung on the tree on a wire, or fastened to a wooden stake or stiff wire stake.

A word of precaution is given here concerning damage sometimes done to growing trees by tying on labels too tightly around small branches with wire or heavy cord. Always fasten the wire so that it will not bind and cut into the branch as the tree grows. Branches may easily be cut through in this way. Always tie labels on loosely or fasten them with small clips.

Labeling your trees greatly increases your enjoyment of them. By some system of marking, records may be kept showing when and where the tree was obtained. Your grounds will also be of greater interest to friends and visitors, who may admire some specimen.

As shown in the illustration at the left, there has quite recently been placed on the market, through seed stores, florists and other stores, a handy, inexpensive series of weather proof labels. These are available in a number of styles to be used in various ways. Illustration furnished through courtesy of Brandt's All Metal Garden Markers.

Chapter XXVII

The Home Nursery

FOR the information of planters who may wish to undertake an extensive planting for a commercial nursery, or for developing their own grounds, some statistics on the trees which may be planted per acre are here given. Owners of country estates and farms will find a home nursery both an interesting and profitable activity. It will not only provide a handy and inexpensive source of supply for Evergreens for the owner's own use, but may also produce a surplus which may be sold.

A home nursery of 1,000 trees such as the one shown on page 131 is made up of fifty trees each of twenty varieties, or one hundred trees each of ten varieties. If the trees are

Set the trees out in rows like the above picture, where you can water and cultivate them.

planted three feet apart in the rows, with rows four feet apart, 12,000 square feet of land is required, which is slightly more than one-fourth acre.

NUMBER OF TREES PER ACRE

The following table shows how many trees can

129

be planted per acre at various distances between the rows and various spacing between the trees in the row.

The distance between the trees in the row will vary with conditions. It will depend on how long the trees are to remain before being again transplanted, and also what particular variety of tree is being planted.

Planting Distances	*Trees per Acre*
Rows 3 feet apart, trees 1 foot apart	14,520
Rows 3 feet apart, trees 2 feet apart	7,260
Rows 3 feet apart, each way	4,840
Rows 4 feet apart, each way	2,725
Rows 5 feet apart, each way	1,745
Rows 6 feet apart, each way	1,210
Rows 8 feet apart, each way	680
Rows 10 feet apart, each way	435
Rows 12 feet apart, each way	300

Should you wish to find the number of trees that can be planted per acre at other distances than those given above, the answer can easily be found in this manner. Multiply the distance in feet between the rows by the distance between the plants in the row. For instance, if the rows are three feet apart and the plants two feet apart in the rows, you would multiply the two together, dividing the result into 43,560 which is the number of square feet in an acre of ground. The result of this division will give the number of trees per acre.

$$2 \times 3 = 6 \text{ sq. ft. occupied by each tree.}$$
$$\text{Square feet per acre—43,560}$$
$$43,560 \div 6 = 7,260$$

NUMBER OF TREES PER BED

When small sizes are transplanted in the nursery into beds, some estimate of the area required can be made from the following figures. If the frame or bed is made six feet wide and one hundred feet long, the following quantities of trees planted at various distances can be planted in a bed:

Planting Distance	*Trees per Bed*
4 x 4 inches	5,400
5 x 5 inches	3,456
6 x 6 inches	2,400
7 x 7 inches	1,763
8 x 8 inches	1,350
10 x 10 inches	864
12 x 12 inches	600

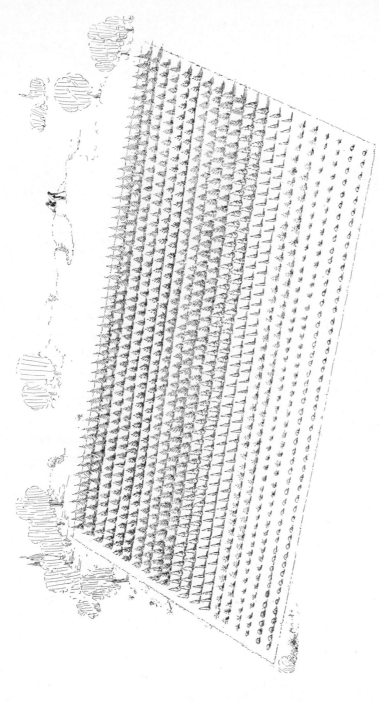

The home nursery should include an assortment of Evergreens of various growing habits, so as to provide a supply of trees for any landscape need. Fifteen to twenty varieties are sufficient to cover any ordinary landscaping project. By planting in rows as shown here, the cultivating may be done by regular farm or garden cultivators, and the upkeep is thus but a small item.

Chapter XXVIII

Diseases, Insect Pests and Injuries

THE first thought which comes to Evergreen owners when they notice anything wrong with their trees is to spray. A weakened and sick-looking Evergreen is not necessarily diseased. Trees which are half-starved, or which have been planted under unfavorable conditions of shade or soil, or have been damaged by severe drought or winter injury, probably do not have any disease and therefore cannot be benefited merely by spraying.

Such trees should be fertilized, kept thoroughly cultivated and watered, or if in a very shady location, they should be removed and replaced with other trees better suited to the location.

It is unfortunate that, frequently, knowledge of tree diseases and pests among home owners is so limited that people are easily taken advantage of by un-scrupulous or ignorant "tree-men," who prey upon this condition and easily persuade home owners to submit to a job of spraying. Often these spraying operations are harmless and may be almost totally useless. Spraying, if done at all, must be done at the right period for the particular pest which is needing attention, in order to do any good.

In almost every community there is a reliable resident nurseryman or prac-tical landscape gardener who will gladly give your trees proper attention. All of the bother of mixing sprays and securing necessary equipment to spray properly can be taken care of at a very small cost. Spraying must be done under the proper pressure to be effective. Most sprays should be applied at a pressure of 200 or 300 pounds and it is often difficult to get this pressure with small hand equipment.

However, for those who prefer to take care of their trees themselves we will attempt to give some information on the more common Evergreen pests.

Again we must mention some of the causes of unhealthy-looking Evergreens which require some treatment besides spraying, to help them: Severe drought, poor soil conditions, starvation, heavy shade, crowding, winter injury, natural shedding of foliage, injury by dogs.

Naturally, these conditions can be corrected only by fertilizing, watering, removing the trees, and replacing them with those of better selection.

When there is definite evidence of disease or insects, the treatment to use can generally be easily determined. If you are in doubt, send a sample of the diseased foliage to your State Entomologist, whose address in most States is

132

either at the State Capitol or at the State University. In sending diseased samples, any information which you can give will be of great help in determining treatment necessary, such as the variety of the tree, how old it is, what location it is planted in, and any other details.

It must be remembered that the treatment of diseases in trees is not an exact science, but one which is constantly being studied by scientific men in the hopes of bettering control measures. It is true also that there are some plant diseases for which there is no effective remedy.

Fortunately, Evergreens in ornamental plantings enjoy comparative freedom from insect and fungus pests as compared to fruit trees and deciduous trees. Trees growing in a highly cultivated state are much less susceptible than trees in different conditions. Very often plantings of ornamental trees will go on from year to year with no difficulty of any kind.

Infestation of insects often comes in cycles. There may be two or three bad years for certain insects, and for natural reasons they may disappear and not be seen again for several years. Certain weather conditions are favorable for promoting the infestations of many diseases of trees.

It must be borne in mind also that spraying and other control measures cannot undo damage already done. They can only prevent further injuries. Any healthy tree, when freed from infestation, has a natural tendency to quickly regain its normal healthy condition.

The Two Main Classes of Insects

For practical purposes insects infesting Evergreens may be classed into two main groups:

1. Chewing Insects—which swallow minute particles of leaves, wood, etc.
2. Sucking Insects—which pierce the tissue of the leaves and the bark, sucking the sap.

Control lies in spraying the chewing insects with some poisonous substance which will cause death when eaten and at the same time not injure the trees. The sucking insects are controlled with a spray of some nature which will cause death by contact or suffocation.

The first step is to determine something of the life cycle of the pest. Many insects are found in the larva stage, emerging into a fly or moth which, in turn, lays the eggs and begins the life cycle over again. Some insects have cocoons or tents. Some have a hard scale-like protection; some produce one brood each year; others may have several broods.

Control measures, therefore, must take into consideration the time of year when the insects are active in feeding. Spraying in the egg stage, or when the insects are covered with a scale of protection, is of little use. Insects which work under the bark, in twigs, trunks or buds, are particularly difficult to control by reason of being almost inaccessible to reach with any spray.

There are dozens of commercially prepared mixtures for spraying available at seed and flower stores and drug stores, put up by manufacturers. When used according to directions most of these sprays are effective for controlling many troublesome pests.

It is well to put in a word of caution particularly in the use of sprays containing oil. Too strong a mixture may severely burn the foliage of Evergreens, especially when in their soft growth. Oil sprays can be more safely used when the trees are in a dormant condition.

CHEWING INSECTS

The following is a brief list of some of the more common chewing insects:

PINE SHOOT MOTH—A larva which works in the buds of Pines. When discovered, cut off and burn the buds. Black Leaf 40 used every 2 or 3 days in June will be beneficial. Black Leaf 40 is commercial nicotine sulphate which is readily obtainable and which is frequently mentioned in these remedies.

PINE LEAF MINER—This pest works in the leaves or needles only and causes the leaves to shrivel and die. The treatment recommended is a miscible oil, one part to 30 parts of water, applied in the spring before the growth starts, at 250 to 300 pounds pressure.

ARBORVITAE LEAF MINER—This miner tunnels in the leaf, which turns it brown or a dull, dead color. The infested twigs and leaves should be cut off and burned. Black Leaf 40 at the rate of one pint to 100 gallons of water, to which is added 4 pounds of laundry soap will be of value in controlling this pest.

BAG WORM—When present in small numbers, the bags can be cut off and burned before the eggs hatch in April. If not discovered until the larvae are at work, spray them with arsenate of lead at the rate of 5 pounds of arsenate of lead to 100 gallons of water.

BORERS AND BARK BEETLES—Various borers infest Evergreens. When this damage is severe, there is no remedy, as it is almost impossible to get at the borers without destroying the trees. Healthy trees are seldom injured. If not too far gone, you can remove the dead, loose bark and the trees may recover. Badly-infested trees should be restored to vigorous condition with fertilizer and watering. Borers cannot operate in trees which are in a strong, healthy condition. Attempts have been made to inject carbon bisulphide into the holes with an eye dropper, sealing them up immediately with paraffin. This treatment is sometimes helpful.

SAW FLIES—At least 8 or 10 different kinds of saw flies infest Evergreens.

Larva of European pine-shoot moth, slightly enlarged, in new growth of red pine. From Dr. W. E. Britton, Entomologist, Connecticut Agricultural Experiment Station.

They curl up the new growth by laying eggs. Sometimes the trees are defoliated by the larvae in the summer. Spray with arsenate of lead at the rate of 4 pounds to 100 gallons of water, adding a little cheap flour so that the spray will stick to the foliage. The saw flies are quite easily shaken off the trees, and, if present on small specimens, a vigorous shaking of the tree will often dislodge them and they will fall to the ground.

In addition to the various chewing insects mentioned, there are many juvenile diseases among Evergreens, which do not concern the planter of ornamental trees. These are generally present in the nursery in the seed beds and in the propagating state. There are also diseases which infest the forests, and, while these diseases are of greater commercial concern and receive the attention of entomologists, many of these diseases are never seen in ornamental plantings.

SUCKING INSECTS

The following is a list of some of the more common sucking insects:

SPRUCE GALL APHID—This aphid makes a pineapple-like growth, killing the tips of the twigs and preventing the growth. It can generally be controlled with miscible oil spray, 1 to 30, before the start of the new growth in the spring.

PINE BARK APHID—This pest makes cottony white masses on trunks and limbs. In summer this can be washed off in some cases with a heavy stream of water or controlled with Black Leaf 40, one pint to 100 gallons of water, to which has been added 4 pounds of soap. This same control is recommended for the Juniper Scale.

SPRUCE BUD SCALE—The same treatment as recommended above when injury is discovered in the summer. However, the solution should be applied under heavy pressure. When discovered in dormant state it can be controlled with the miscible oil spray previously mentioned.

RED SPIDER—In hot, dry, summer weather, Red Spider multiplies rapidly. The injury from this pest is conspicuous on Evergreens which become a rusty color. Spruce and some Junipers are more apt to be infested than some other families of Evergreens. The presence of very small white webs sometimes indicates the presence of the spider, but to see the spider itself requires exceptional eyesight or a microscope. When the pest does establish itself, oftentimes heavy rain will wash them off entirely, and they will not become established again during that season. It is also sometimes possible to eradicate them by spraying the tree with a stiff stream of water. There are a number of good commercial sprays effective in the control of this pest.

A good spray is Black Leaf 40, made by mixing one pint of Black Leaf 40 to 100 gallons of water, to which is added one and one-half gallons of molasses, smaller quantities in proportion. Thoroughness is the keynote of success in spraying. The more pressure, and the better the coverage, the better the chances of effective control.

CEDAR APPLES—Junipers, including some of the horticultural varieties, are sometimes attacked by a fungus, commonly called Cedar Apple. In order for this fungus to complete its life cycle, it must spend a part of its life on apples, quince, hawthornes or some similar tree. Cedar Apple is a soft, spongy, brownish-yellow growth often seen, especially after wet weather. On account of this pest, it is a good plan to avoid planting Junipers in a position where they will be in

Young spruce galls, and cottony covering of empty egg-masses. Michigan State College, East Lansing, Mich.

Pine Bark Aphid. Michigan State College, East Lansing, Mich.

close proximity to apple trees. About the only suggestion that can be made to control this fungus is to take off the growths when they appear on the tree. This can easily be done if the trees are small and there are only a few of them. Where the number of trees runs into any quantity, about the only thing to do is to remove either the apple trees or the Juniper trees.

WINTER BROWNING—While this condition is not a disease it may easily be mistaken as such. We quote a brief discussion of this difficulty from the Bulletin of the Arnold Arboretum, Series 3, Vol. VI, Nos. 1 and 2: "In the early spring, before there is any external evidence of growth, coniferous foliage sometimes exhibits a rather sudden browning. The extent of the browning varies from a touch here and there, to extensive patches, or an inclusion of the entire crown, in the last instances the plants appearing as though dead. This injury is most pronounced in the foliage produced the preceding year, though it may extend to needles of all ages. Not infrequently, twigs as well as the leaves may be killed outright. No species are wholly immune, whether of Pines, Spruces, Firs, Arborvitaes, etc., but some are more susceptible than others. Browning occurs almost exclusively on the sunned side of the crowns, and in the case of trees is most

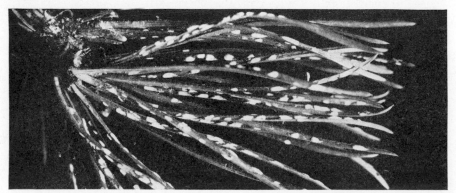

Pine leaf scale. Michigan State College, East Lansing, Mich.

severe in the lower branches. If there is nothing more than a browning of the foliage, the subsequent new growth restores the green aspect of the crowns, and little permanent injury results. If twigs are killed there is a dwarfing of branches on the southerly exposed sides, and in most severe cases plants may be killed outright.

"The cause of 'Winter browning' has been ascribed by some observers to excessive loss of moisture at a time when the ground is still frozen and the roots are unable to make good the losses.

"Avoidance of browning is desirable, especially in the more tender conifers. This can be provided by temporary shelter or protective plantings."

INJURY FROM DOGS—Frequent visits from male dogs cause Evergreen foliage within reach to turn black and die. For this difficulty there is nothing to do but to keep the dogs away.

The most effective means is to surround each tree with a low wire fence. This is objectionable, however, because of appearance.

A device called the Garden Club Shrubbery Protector has proven an effective barrier. It is so constructed that it cannot harm the dog. The Protector is a unit of steel spring wires, rust-proofed to last indefinitely. They are flexible and cannot tear clothing of passersby. Each Protector has three prongs and covers a quarter of a circle. Four Protectors will completely protect a shrub on all sides. Or, if the shrub is against the house or wall, two Protectors are enough. It costs little and is not noticed from even a few feet away.

Various chemical compounds designed to be hung on the tree in tubes or sacks, or sprayed on it, are on the market. Some of these chemicals may be of temporary value, but we are unable to recommend them through actual trial.

SOURCES OF INFORMATION

The following booklets contain the most complete information available on the subject of Evergreen pests. They include an extensive description of each insect, its life cycle, together with control measures. They also contain illustrations of many of the more common insects. They are available at a small cost.

"Extension Bulletin No. 76. Some Common Sucking Insect Pests of Evergreens."—Michigan State College, East Lansing, Michigan.

"Circular Bulletin No. 141. Some Chewing Insects Infesting Michigan Evergreens."—Michigan State College, East Lansing, Michigan.

TREE SURGERY

Within recent years wonderful progress has been made through the science of Tree-Surgery, in preserving valuable trees by scientific feeding, trimming and repairing of cavities. Anyone having valuable and old trees, in particular, should secure the services of one of the well known organizations who are prepared both by experience and equipment to render service of this nature.

Part III

USES OF EVERGREENS

Foundation-Plantings, Outdoor Living Rooms,
Hedges and Other Uses

Chapter XXIX

Notes on Landscaping and the Use of Evergreens

LANDSCAPE gardening on any extensive scale involves problems for the professional landscape architect. The grades, the drives, and the location of buildings are first considerations.

Where circumstances permit, the landscaping should be done under the guidance of a landscape architect. His services are just as important as the building architect. It will often prove a great saving in the end to have a plan prepared covering the entire property. The actual work may extend over several years, and may be carried out by anyone qualified to follow the architect's plan. Under a haphazard arrangement of planting, costly and disappointing mistakes can easily be made.

The suggestions as given here are intended only for the simple improvements home owners may wish to make, themselves, including such plantings as foundations of houses, entrances, hedges, outdoor living rooms, and the like.

Quite recently an interesting book was published by the Harvard University School of Landscape Architecture entitled, "Landscape Architecture—A Classified Bibliography." In it are printed the names of more than three thousand published books and pamphlets covering every conceivable detail of landscape design and construction. Few human pursuits have been given greater attention throughout the world, and there is no end of information available for anyone who may wish to study any particular phase of this interesting subject.

The making of lawns, laying out flower beds, the use of shade trees and shrubs, vines and fruit trees, are all subjects beyond the scope of our present

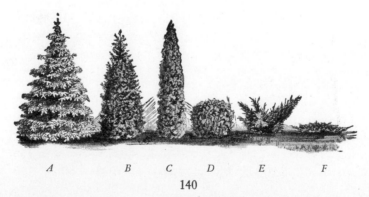

A   B   C   D   E   F

140

interest. Large areas have need of all these things. We shall confine suggestions to the use of Evergreen trees.

Evergreens have many natural advantages over other kinds of plants. There is an increasing appreciation of Evergreens by home owners and a growing popularity of these trees. Their use is limited only by a lack of knowledge as to how to select the different varieties to best advantage. Evergreens are persistent. They remain from season to season and from year to year. They offer a surprising variety of colors at different seasons. They do not quickly grow out of bounds. Because of their many shapes, Evergreens provide a proper selection of varieties suitable for any planting need.

We are interested in knowing Evergreens from the standpoint of the growing habit of the tree, as it relates to the proper use of the tree in various landscaping projects. We may, for convenience, divide Evergreens roughly into six groups according to their natural habit of growth. Please refer to the sketch. We must bear in mind that the same tree will often behave differently under various conditions of climate, exposure, soil, and cultural treatment.

Frequent reference will be made to these groups throughout the following pages. Obviously two major problems are involved when we undertake a landscape improvement; first, the purpose of the planting to be made, and, secondly, the selection of trees to be used. There is naturally more than one variety suitable for any particular need. For example: A foundation planting may be composed of one or a dozen different varieties which may be of similar growing habit. The thing to avoid is using a type of tree whose growing habit is not suitable.

It is not practical to make a classification according to growing habit of all the known cultivated Evergreens which are listed on pages 40 to 60. The lists which follow contain only the Evergreens most commonly used in the vicinity of Chicago. Before purchasing other varieties, planters should determine in which of these six groups a tree belongs, so that the tree will prove suited to its proposed location.

Varieties for a Shady Location

For planting locations on the north side of the house, or in any location which is very shady, use Hemlocks and Yews wherever possible. Pfitzer Juniper and Mugho Pine will also do well in partial shade.

Tall-Growing Evergreens, Group A

Trees in this group are the largest and tallest-growing forms. They include varieties which develop into specimens ten to fifteen feet in diameter and up to a height of fifty feet or more. They are suitable for heavy backgrounds, screens, windbreaks, forest plantings, and individual specimens. Planters very often use them in other ways, but in doing so, must realize that the trees will eventually become too large and must be removed. Some varieties, however, can be trimmed and kept small for a time.

Abies arizonica (Cork Fir)
        ”   concolor (White Fir)
        ”   fraseri (Fraser Fir)
Picea alcockiana (Alcock Spruce)
        ”   canadensis (White Spruce)
        ”   canadensis albertiana (Black Hill Spruce)
        ”   engelmanni (Engelmann Spruce)
        ”   excelsa (Norway Spruce)
        ”   polita (Tigertail Spruce)
        ”   pungens (Colorado Spruce)
        ”   pungens kosteriana (Koster Blue Spruce)
Pinus banksiana (Jack Pine)
        ”   cembra (Swiss Stone Pine)
        ”   nigra (Austrian Pine)
        ”   ponderosa (Western Yellow Pine)
        ”   resinosa (Red or Norway Pine)
        ”   strobus (White Pine)
        ”   sylvestris (Scotch Pine)
Pseudotsuga douglasi (Douglas Fir)
Tsuga canadensis (Canada Hemlock)

Medium Height Evergreens, Group B

The average height of trees in this group will run eight to twenty feet, and in diameter usually not more than three to five feet. Such trees are suitable for the taller-growing specimens in foundation plantings, entrance groups; also, suitable for planting in borders to add contrast to flowering shrubs, or formal uses in gardens. All trees in this group, particularly Junipers and Arborvitaes, may be easily kept within bounds by pruning.

Chamaecyparis pisifera (Sawara Cypress)
    ”   ”   var. aurea (Golden Sawara Cypress)
    ”   ”   var. filifera (Thread Retinospora)
    ”   ”   var. filifera aurea (Golden Thread Retinospora)
    ”   ”   var. filifera nana (Dwarf Thread Retinospora)
    ”   ”   var. plumosa (Plume Retinospora)
    ”   ”   var. plumosa aurea (Golden Plume Retinospora)
    ”   ”   var. squarrosa (Moss Retinospora)
Juniperus chinensis (Chinese Juniper)
    ”   ”   var. albo-variegata (Whiteleaf Chinese Juniper)
    ”   ”   var. neaboriensis (Also known as J. macrocarpa)
    ”   communis var. suecica (Swedish Juniper)
    ”   excelsa   var. stricta (Spiny Greek Juniper)
    ”   scopulorum (Colorado Juniper)
    ”   ”   var. Hill Silver Juniper

Juniperus virginiana (Redcedar)
        "   "   var. burki (Burk Juniper)
        "   "   var. cannarti (Cannart Redcedar)
        "   "   var. elegantissima (Goldtip Redcedar)
        "   "   var. glauca (Silver Redcedar)
        "   "   var. keteleeri (Keteleer Redcedar)
        "   "   var. schotti (Schott Redcedar)
Taxus cuspidata capitata (Japanese Yew)
    " media var. hatfieldi (Hatfield Yew)
    " media var. hicksi (Hicks Yew)
Thuya occidentalis (American Arborvitae)
        "   "   var. douglasi aurea (Douglas Golden Arborvitae)
        "   "   var. hoveyi (Hovey Arborvitae)
        "   "   var. lutea (Geo. Peabody Arborvitae)
        "   "   var. rosenthali (Rosenthal Arborvitae)
        "   "   var. vervaeneana (Vervaene Arborvitae)
        "   "   var. wareana (Siberian Arborvitae)

NARROW PYRAMIDAL EVERGREENS, GROUP C

This group covers trees of extremely narrow, pyramidal habit. The narrow growth may be helped by trimming, but all of them have a tendency to produce very narrow spire-like forms. Such trees are of use at entrances for sentinels, also for markers in formal gardens, at corners of houses, and similar situations. All of these forms can easily be trimmed and kept small if desired, although some of these varieties will reach twelve to fifteen feet or more when matured.

Juniperus chinensis var. pyramidalis (Column Chinese Juniper)
    " communis var. hibernica (Irish Juniper)
    " virginiana var. pyramidalis hilli (Hill Pyramidal Juniper)
    "   " var. pyramidiformia hilli (Hill Dundee Juniper)
Thuya occidentalis var. douglasi pyramidalis (Douglas Pyramidal Arborvitae)
    "   " var. pyramidalis (Pyramidal Arborvitae)

ROUND OR GLOBULAR EVERGREENS, GROUP D

There is increasing need for round or ball-shaped trees. For use around smaller types of houses, in foundation plantings, in corners next to the walk, and in many situations where "tree forms" would be out of the question, these little, dwarf-growing trees fill the purpose. They can all be trimmed and kept as small as desired, although if allowed to grow, many of these trees will reach a size and diameter of three or four feet.

Juniperus virginiana var. globosa (Globe Redcedar)
Picea excelsa var. maxwelli (Maxwell Spruce)
    "   " var. nidiformis (Nest-shaped Spruce)
Pinus mugho var. mughus (Dwarf Mugho Pine)
Thuya occidentalis var. compacta (Parsons Arborvitae)
    "   " var. globosa (Globe Arborvitae)

Thuya occidentalis var. little gem
      „   „   var. umbraculifera
      „   „   var. woodwardi (Woodward Arborvitae)

HALF ERECT EVERGREENS, GROUP E

Among the half-erect forms we find many of the finest of all our Evergreens and those which are of greatest use, especially in landscape planting of small areas. Trees in this group include those forms which are essential for the low-growing trees in foundation-plantings, entrance-plantings, rock gardens, and low-growing groups.

Juniperus chinensis var. pfitzeriana (Pfitzer Juniper)
  „   communis var. depressa (Prostrate Juniper)
  „   „   var. depressa aurea (Golden Prostrate Juniper)
  „   „   var. depressa plumosa (Andorra Juniper)
  „   „   var. depressa vase shaped
  „   sabina (Savin Juniper)
  „   „   var. pyramidalis (Pyramidal Savin Juniper)
  „   „   var. von ehron (Von Ehron Juniper)
  „   squamata var. meyeri (Meyer Juniper)
  „   virginiana var. kosteri (Koster Redcedar)
Pinus densiflora var. umbraculifera (Japanese Umbrella Pine)
Taxus canadensis (American Yew)
  „   cuspidata var. andersoni (Anderson Yew)
  „   „   var. browni (Brown Yew)
  „   „   var. nana (Dwarf Japanese Yew)

CREEPING EVERGREENS, GROUP F

Trees in this group are the low, creeping, mat-like forms that remain close to the ground. They grow not over six or eight inches high under usual conditions and spread to a considerable diameter. However, as they can easily be clipped and trimmed, they remain for years in a small space. Trees in this group are suitable for rock gardens, to cover terraces or banks, or to finish off a group of taller-growing forms.

Juniperus chinensis var. sargenti (Sargent Juniper)
  „   horizontalis var. douglasi (Waukegan Juniper)
  „   japonica (Japanese Juniper)
  „   „   var. aureovariegata (Variegated Dwarf Japanese Juniper)
  „   „   var. nana (Hill Japanese Juniper)
  „   sabina   var. horizontalis (Bar Harbor Juniper)

Chapter XXX

Foundation Planting

ONE of the main uses of Evergreens for owners of suburban homes is the foundation-planting. No matter how small the lot may be, with no opportunity for other features, the area immediately around the house generally receives first attention. There is, of course, much thoughtless planting done, and many neglected plantings which add nothing in artistic beauty. Types of homes vary too, of course. No one design can be followed that will be equally attractive to all styles of houses. However, in the following pages we have made many suggestions and pointed out some common mistakes.

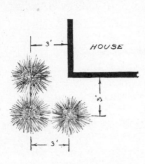

ALLOW AT LEAST THREE FEET BETWEEN TREES

It is easier to change the planting on paper than it is to change the planting afterwards. For this reason it is always an excellent idea to first make a sketch of the planting which you propose to make. To do this to best advantage, accurately draw an outline of the house on ruled paper like the sketch below. If you let each square represent one foot, you will then be sure to get the planting done in correct proportion. In this way you can tell exactly how much space there is between windows, doors, etc., and also the number of trees required can be more accurately estimated.

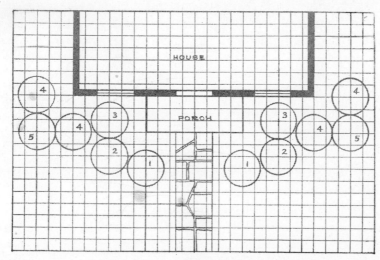

145

Laying Out the Foundation Planting

The size of the house, the height of the foundation, and the matter of economy are all factors which govern the number of trees necessary or desirable for a planting. Below are shown four different treatments for the same house.

This series of sketches illustrates the evolution of a planting from the simplest form up to the completed, heavy type of planting. From the standpoint of economy a planting of this kind may be developed over a period of two or three years. The first year the house could be planted as shown in the first group; the second year few trees planted, and so on.

(1) Simple entrance design

In planting "1" the simplest possible planting is shown. A tree of upright habit on either side of the entrance, with a group of one or two low-growing forms around it.

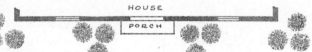

(2) Addition of trees to corners

Planting "2" shows the same design with the addition of groups at corners.

(3) Complete foundation treatment

Planting "3" shows the same planting with the area between corners and the entrance filled in by using low-growing trees beneath the windows.

(4) For large homes

In group "4," where space allows, and the house is of a suitable style, the planting may be extended to include two rows of Evergreens rounded out both at the entrance and at the corners of the house.

Choice of Material

For either side of entrance and at corners of house use trees in group B or group C. Under windows and in foreground use trees in group D and group E.

These sketches show three plantings for the same house. The planting above, composed of overgrown shrubs and poor choice of material, is typical of many foundation plantings. Not only are the shrubs bare in winter, but they obstruct the view from windows. They detract from, rather than add to, the appearance of the house.

By contrast, this planting is neat and attractive. The trees at the corners and at the entrance might be made up of trees from group B. Under the windows use trees of group D or group E.

This is the same planting as the one above with additional trees added. Reference to the various groups of Evergreens on pages 141 to 144 will suggest an extensive choice of material to carry out such a planting.

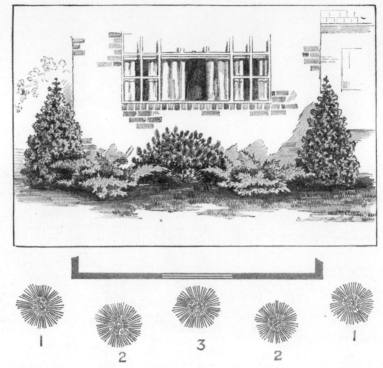

Planting Key: 1. American Arborvitae. 2. Pfitzer Juniper. 3. Hill Mugho Pine.

Two planting plans for the same space are illustrated on this page. The arrangement pictured above is the one which the landscape architect would recommend. This planting has a variation in height which gives it a more artistic finish, and which the eye will readily recognize as an improvement over the picture below. The trees in the planting above are not set in one straight line, but the two Junipers are spaced slightly in front of the others, giving the whole an appearance which should serve as an example of artistic treatment. The planting idea which this picture illustrates is one which can be made use of in any foundation planting. Briefly: avoid lines which are too straight and stiff.

An Example of Poor Selection and Good Selection

Sometimes the right way of planting becomes more evident by a study of the wrong methods. On this page the same house is shown. One picture with a poor placing of trees and wrong selection of types, and the other with careful arrangement and proper selection of varieties.

In the picture at the bottom of this page the round trees at the entrance are out of place. Also, many large-growing Spruces and Pines have been used which are not appropriate. Out in the lawn is a Juniper of slender branched pyramidal form. Trees of this type should never be used as specimens. The Spruce, as shown in upper picture, is a much better choice. Due regard must also be made for shade. Not all varieties will do well in the shade. A list of varieties for the shade is given elsewhere in this chapter.

Picture at the right shows a good planting arrangement.

The trees numbered 1, 4 and 5 could be any tree of group B or group C. Trees numbered 2 and 3 could be any tree of groups D or E. Trees numbered 6 any tree in group A.

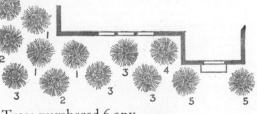

The planting below shows poor selection of varieties as explained above.

Number 1 Pyramidal Arborvitae. Number 2 Savin Juniper. Number 3 Mugho Pine. Number 4 Andorra Juniper. Number 5 Pfitzer Juniper.

For trees labelled number 1, any trees of groups B and C might be used. For trees labelled 2, 3, 4, and 5 any trees in groups D and E would be suitable. This is a south exposure. For a shady location, Yews would be more satisfactory than Arborvitae and Junipers.

Simple plantings are generally the most pleasing. A few, healthy, well-cared-for trees of suitable selection give that pleasing dignity and beauty we so much admire. The tall trees in this picture are Cannart Redcedar. They might be any similar Juniper or Arborvitae. In a shady location Hemlock or Yew would be suitable. The low-growing trees below the window are Pfitzer Juniper.

Different types of house construction require different kinds of plantings. Almost all foundation plantings, however, need to be made up of trees of contrasting habit, tall narrow trees surrounded by lower ones. The taller trees should be of groups B or C; lower-growers of groups D and E. Your own choice of colors and foliage characteristics should determine the actual variety. For a screen as shown in background of picture, choose tall, bushy growing trees such as those in group A. The rules for selection of varieties are really quite simple, if the

suggestions regarding the *growing habit* of the trees are followed.

Entrance planting at the residence of Mr. and Mrs. A. H. Hill,
Dundee, Illinois.

The entrance planting shown at bottom of page 151, is the residence of Mr. and Mrs. A. H. Hill, Dundee, Illinois. Effectively used, for tall trees are trimmed specimens of Cannart Redcedar. Lower-growers are Yews. The creeping Evergreens along the walk are Bar Harbor Junipers. These might be any of the several varieties of creeping Evergreens listed under group F.

SIMPLE PLANTING FOR A SMALL HOME

A few, well-chosen Evergreens may easily transform a bare and drab house into an inviting and cheerful home. There is no place here for Spruces, Firs and large Pines. Rather we should choose Junipers, Arborvitaes and Yews. At the entrance and corners use trees in groups B and C. Beneath windows, use trees in groups D and E. The actual trees in this planting are Pyramidal Arborvitae, Spreading Japanese Yew, beneath windows Pfitzer Juniper and Andorra Juniper. There are other combinations, of course, of similar habit of growth which would be just as attractive.

A good selection in keeping with the modest sized home.

THE FOUNDATION PLANTING IN ITS SIMPLEST FORM

The charm of many plantings of Evergreens often lies in the simplicity of a single tree of the right type, placed in an appropriate relation to its surroundings. Such a tree, of course, comes under close scrutiny and must, therefore, be kept in an attractive, thrifty condition.

Houses and buildings of fine construction, such as the one at the left, need fewer trees for decoration. This single specimen of Arborvitae satisfies the eye.

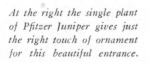

At the right the single plant of Pfitzer Juniper gives just the right touch of ornament for this beautiful entrance.

1. *Globe Arborvitae.*
2. *Douglas Golden Arborvitae.*
3. *Mugho Pine.*
4. *Waukegan Juniper.*
5. *Berckman Arborvitae.*
6. *Cannart Redcedar.*
7. *Schott Redcedar.*
8. *Redcedar.*
9. *Pfitzer Juniper.*
10. *Japanese Yew.*
11. *Chinese Juniper.*
12. *American Arborvitae.*

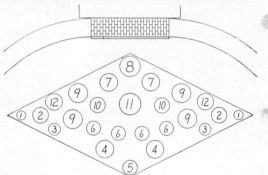

Entrance Bed Planting

An unusual entrance such as this one offers opportunity for a unique grouping of dwarf and slow-growing Evergreens. When made up of brightly-contrasting colors and variations of foliage, it makes a year-round point of interest. While the trees are rather close together, they may be easily kept within bounds for many years by pruning. Such a group should consist of Junipers, Yews and Arborvitaes. In other climates various forms of Cypress may be used. The taller-growers are used in back, lower-growers in front. A suggested list of varieties is shown with the planting sketch. The tall trees next to the house are Redcedar.

This planting shows a good choice of material and an interesting variation of color. The tall trees are Silver Redcedar. The low trees, Andorra Juniper. Others in the group are Pfitzer Juniper, Dwarf Japanese Yew, Mugho Pine, Globe Juniper, and at extreme left for the shady corner, a Hemlock. Such a grouping when kept cultivated, fertilized, watered and pruned, will make an attractive planting for many years.

Chapter XXXI

The Outdoor Living Room

THE area at the rear of the house was for many years known only as the "back yard." It has only been within the past few years that the opportunities which these areas around the home offer have been fully realized and taken advantage of. Even today, however, there are probably less than twenty per cent of the back yards of American homes which have been even partially developed.

The outdoor living room should be practical as well as ornamental. There should be areas set aside for attractive flower beds, groups of trees and shrubs, areas for lawn games, perhaps an outdoor fireplace, lawn seats, chairs, swings, tables and, in fact, any features which will make this part of the grounds attractive and livable.

Where gardens are very limited in size, it is often advisable to avoid too much in the way of garden features, but allow as much space as possible for open lawn. A low Evergreen hedge with an archway covered with climbing roses makes an attractive approach to this small area adorned only with a single garden seat. Flagstone walks set in cement are more appropriate for landscape designs of this nature than cement. Walks made of cinders or gravel are less expensive and when edged properly are very appropriate. Although this area is limited, there is still opportunity for the use of Evergreens, and doubly so, because of the close proximity of adjoining property and buildings.

One delightful feature of the outdoor living room, which is easily provided, and which will prove a source of pleasure, is the home picnic ground. There is much pleasure to be derived from lunches eaten in the open in your own grounds. In place of the table and umbrella shown in this sketch a home constructed table with seats attached will accommodate a large group. Flagstone makes an ideal ground covering for this sort of a feature, where it is frequently used, especially if it is rather shady, where grass does not make luxuriant growth. Evergreens naturally have a part in the development of this feature of the outdoor living room. Trees which are used in the background in this planting might be any variety of trees in group "B" with others of groups "D," "E" and "F" used in the foreground. The list which designates these groups of Evergreens is shown on pages 141 to 144.

Where it is possible to make it so, the outdoor living room should be in close proximity to the house. If it can be arranged so that a vista of the area can be seen from the house itself, this is, of course, a desirable arrangement.

Privacy is another feature which must be given first consideration. Naturally, we prefer our outdoor living room to be shielded from adjoining property and from passersby.

To begin with, the area available should be carefully measured and drawn to scale on ruled paper. Existing features, such as trees, walks and buildings can be located on the plan, and the other additional features to be added can then be planned and arranged properly. It is easier to change a plan on paper than to make any change after the planting is completed.

Shade is greatly to be desired in the outdoor living room, and unless shade trees already exist they should be planted in such a position that they will provide shade over a certain part of the area at least.

There is no set style or arrangement which will be equally adaptable to all homes, but there are several essential features which can be incorporated into almost any design. In the several pages which we have devoted to the subject "The Outdoor Living Room," we have shown about a dozen different designs, some of which may perhaps prove helpful in the arrangement of your grounds. On homesites of limited size it is often desirable to include a rock garden and perhaps a pool in connection with the outdoor living room. This may be either formal in design, or it may be a naturalistic pool, in which case it should be arranged at some corner of the ground, rather than in the center of the lawn.

Almost without exception, any outdoor living room which has attracted your attention has as its foundation an attractive, well-kept, green lawn. Do not hesitate to allow as much space as possible for the grass. Keep the center of the lawn open, with plantings and features around the edge. This arrangement will generally prove more attractive than a type of planting which cuts up the area into too many small sections.

The boundary of the lot can generally be planted with a mass of Evergreens or shrubs to serve both as a screen from the adjoining property and as a back-

Again in this sketch we have shown the advantage of obtaining elevation in the rear of the outdoor living room. This not only gives a better view of the garden while sitting in the garden seat, but offers more interesting opportunities for the planting of flowers and Evergreens on the slope. This little nook can be constructed in one of the far corners of the outdoor living room, with a view towards the house, or some other feature, such as a pool, or beds of flowers. In a planting of this kind there is an opportunity for extensive use of Evergreens of the more dwarf types, such as the trees suggested on pages 143 and 144 in groups "D," "E" and "F." Taller specimens, of course, must be used in the background.

ground for beds of perennials, annuals or roses. Any feature such as a garden house, or a bench, or lawn seat will generally look best when set at the greatest distance from the house. Anyone who sits in the garden house or bench will then have a view of the entire area.

No one can explain the certain livable touch which invades some outdoor living rooms and is lacking in others. This is a matter of harmony in arrangement and choice of materials. We find the same condition in the interior of the house. Some rooms which may be elegantly furnished, are cold and uninviting. On the other hand, another room which may be furnished at very modest cost is appealing to us and has a certain atmosphere which we can sense but cannot always explain or understand. We are aware of the pleasing effect of the whole but may not easily determine exactly why the room appeals to us. After all, it reminds us somewhat of the answer which was given by a great artist who was once asked, "With what do you mix your paints?" The artist's answer was short and to the point. "Brains," he said.

Every family has different demands on the outdoor living room, depending upon the family, their routine of living, and their taste.

We must not overlook the children in planning our outdoor living rooms. Play grounds do not necessarily need to detract in any way from the beauty of the grounds. A small area such as this occupies but small space, but provides contentment for children. There is also the added security that comes from knowing that children are at play in complete safety. As a background for a feature of this kind Evergreens are useful. Select trees of groups "A" and "B" for the taller specimens.

At some point in the outdoor living room, generally near the rear of the lot, is the suitable location for a bench or garden seat, as illustrated in this sketch. If the bench is adjacent to a formal pool or lily pond, this makes the bench still more useful and appropriate. The various Evergreens which are suggested here may be composed of many varieties so long as they conform to the various groups as indicated. Reference to the trees which may be selected from these different groups will be found on pages 141 to 144.

This outdoor living room and Evergreen garden, shown on following page, are a feature in the grounds of Mr. and Mrs. A. H. Hill, Dundee, Illinois. The photographer stood in approximately the same position in taking both pictures, one looking toward the house and the other in the opposite direction. An outdoor living room of this nature includes many features. First, the well-kept expanse of grass with ample space for flowers, both perennials and annuals, around the border. The rock garden and pool at the rear have been built on a slight elevation, with a loose rock wall providing opportunity for many interesting and unusual flowering plants which thrive under such a condition. Any rock wall should have an open, sunny location, preferably exposed to the south. This pool is quite large, only one-half of the pool and garden being shown in this picture. The two wooden bridges lead to an additional area further on, devoted to flowering lilacs, tulips and annuals.

A wide variety of dwarf and slow-growing Evergreens are included in this design. Many forms of Junipers, dwarf Pines, Spruces, and others, are planted in their proper relation to the entire picture. Taller Evergreens have been used as a background and as an outline to the area.

Garden at the residence of Mr. and Mrs. A. H. Hill, Dundee, Illinois.

This photograph taken by the eminent Dr. L. H. Bailey, noted horticulturist, who visited this garden in the summer of 1932.

The various illustrations which are shown in these pages contain the suggestions for the essential features of the outdoor living room. They vary in their design from the formal to the semi-formal and naturalistic treatment, offering suggestions for almost any type of design to suit the location and the taste of the planter.

As the three pictures on page 163 show, there may be different designs for the outdoor living room which may be used for the same grounds. It will be seen that these three sketches represent the same lot with the garage in each case in the same position. In the formal style of planting, (figure 1), the lines are straight and the areas are of geometrical design. Space is provided for beds of flowers, and the lawn is kept open except for a rectangular pool. As in the case of the other designs also, Evergreens are used as a background, at the end of the lot, as well as in groups.

In the semi-formal plan, (figure 2), there is an area immediately adjoining the living room which is arranged in informal and irregular design, and an additional area in the rear devoted to a small vegetable garden and a flower garden. A garden shelter is situated so as to give a view of the flower arrangement. Note also that there is a bird bath in the center of the garden and an arch gate leading

While this particular feature is not actually a part of the outdoor living room, it forms an interesting approach to it. It represents an unusual treatment in the nature of a rear or side entrance leading to the garden beyond. Evergreens of the proper selection, as indicated, add considerably to this appealing and attractive design.

to the vegetable garden. In choosing the design of any garden of this sort, one must bear in mind that these formal designs require considerable time to maintain them. It is, of course, useless to attempt such a design unless everything is kept neat and in perfect order.

The naturalistic treatment, (figure 3), is likely the one that will appeal to most people. Evergreens play a prominent part in this plan, both in the outline of the entire garden, as well as in various groups and specimens used in the rock garden and around the pool. There is less work of maintenance in a living room of this design than in the other designs shown here. The open expanse of lawn, the background of colorful Evergreens, make a most pleasing picture.

Figure 2.
The semi-formal plan provides a formal garden and space for a vegetable garden.

Figure 1.
A more or less formal treatment with Evergreen hedges and background.

Figure 3.
The naturalistic treatment combining an Evergreen border with a pool and rock garden.

Any means by which a change of the level in the garden can be accomplished adds an interesting feature. It will be seen in this picture that the garden shelter is a slight elevation above the level of the lawn. It is approached with a rise of two steps. There is also a low wall of loose rocks behind which is an area devoted to flowers. An added feature of interest is the small lily pond surrounded with a well chosen group of Evergreens. The various groups, as indicated, refer to the type or form of Evergreens which may be selected to give this effect. By referring to pages 141 to 144 a suggested list of various kinds of Evergreens of these different groups will enable anyone to make proper selection.

In making your plan, prepare it in such a way that there are inviting nooks, seats, walks, benches, shelters, arches, gates, fountains, sun dials, bird baths, stepping stones, and all such garden accessories.

Another advantage of making a plan is to work towards a definite arrangement over a period of years. It is not necessary, when you have a plan, to carry out the entire plan at any one time; it may take several seasons, but you will know that when you have finished you have a well planned and arranged garden. This planned arrangement will be in sharp contrast to the type of planting which proceeds with poorly thought out features added at intervals, perhaps without proper consideration.

Evergreens have a very definite place in an outdoor living room. Where plantings are composed entirely of shrubs and flowers the outdoor living room is barren and uninteresting except during the summer. When Evergreens form the background of the grounds, they are on duty at all seasons. They are attractive in summer, and even in the winter when covered with snow, they can never fail to be a source of interest.

CHAPTER XXXII

Specimen-Planting

IN choosing a tree for planting as an individual specimen, two main considerations must receive attention. We must select a type of tree with tall upright growth and wide spreading branches which makes a shapely symmetrical growth, one that grows old gracefully, adding to its charm and beauty as years go on.

Then we must also consider its location. So as to give room for full future development, a specimen tree should be planted at least ten to fifteen feet away from buildings or other trees. No tree can maintain a luxuriant growth and keep its lower limbs if it is too crowded or shaded. This location should also be chosen carefully with regard to a pleasing view, either from some window in the house or some point in the garden.

Among the Evergreens in northern Illinois and localities of similar climate, the Colorado Blue Spruce and its well known variety, the Koster Blue Spruce, will doubtless continue

The living Christmas tree! It gives joy to the owner and cheer to all. Spruces are ideal Christmas Trees.

165

to be the most popular for individual specimens. Their spectacular color and their tendency to develop a well balanced growth give these trees preference. In former years the Norway Spruce was widely used. While not so popular now it still has many admirers. Other excellent trees for specimens are Douglas Fir, Concolor Fir, Black Hill Spruce, Austrian Pine, and White Pine.

Various Junipers and Arborvitae, as well as dwarf species of Evergreens, are not suited to this type of planting.

Quite recently there has been a wide-spread interest in decorating specimens with electric lights at Christmas. Certainly Evergreens should be used in this way as they spread good cheer to everyone. However, in using large bulbs, avoid resting them directly on the foliage as the heat may dry out the foliage and injure it. Let the lights be suspended from the branches so that no damage will occur.

Generally speaking, it is poor practice to set specimen trees directly in front of the house if it is near the street. If this is the only area available the appearance will be better if the trees are planted closer to the outer edge of the lot.

*Colorado Blue Spruces win the admiration of all lovers
of trees.*

Chapter XXXIII

Evergreens for Screens and Heavy Borders

Proper Selections for Groups

BECAUSE of their persistent foliage, Evergreens are ideal for permanent screens against adjacent unsightly views. They also make ideal subjects for hillsides, heavy backgrounds, and similar uses around extensive homes.

For such purposes trees of wide-spreading branches and upright growth should be used for the trees in the farthest background. Such plantings in the climate of northern Illinois should include various Spruces, Firs and Pines. If room permits, such plantings may be faced with some of the more dwarf and slow-

White Pine spaced about ten feet apart make an effective screen.

growing types of Evergreens, including the Junipers, the Yews and the Arbor-vitae, as well as the dwarf Mugho Pine.

The question of what varieties to use together in groups is one difficult to answer. It might be said, however, that as a general rule trees of the same genera, or family, even though they may be of contrasting colors, look better when arranged in a group than trees of greatly contrasting foliage. For example: A small grouping of trees might consist of several kinds of Junipers composed of those with blue foliage, green foliage and here and there a yellow-foliage variety. Such a grouping is more pleasing in appearance than one made up of tall, heavy, coarse-growing Pines, combined with fine-textured Junipers and Arborvitae.

Plantings should be made, of course, primarily to suit the fancy of the planter and the owner of the property. Sometimes a peculiar like or dislike is responsible for many special arrangements of trees. A variety of trees which might appeal to one person might be distasteful to another. It is, therefore, largely a matter of taste as to what combination may be chosen for any particular grouping of Evergreens.

The foregoing remarks can only be given in the nature of general suggestions for anyone who wishes to avoid mistakes in the proper choice of trees for various purposes.

For heavy screens and borders use tall growers in back with low growers in foreground. The tree in this foreground is a Mugho Pine.

Chapter XXXIV

How to Build a Pool

ROCK gardens and pools are examples of the most interesting and intensive forms of horticulture. The exact form or style of the garden gives opportunity for endless variety. On this and following pages, different pools and rockeries are shown. Rockeries are usually considered distinct from pools; although, on grounds of limited space, a combination of a pool and rockery often gives opportunity for a most interesting treatment.

Some pools may be built using a clay basin. Concrete, however, is the most practical material for building the basin of the pool and is recommended.

In the drawing shown below details of construction of a simple pool are shown.

First comes the selection of the site. Wherever a hillside or an uneven, rough piece of land is available, this makes an attractive site for the pool. However, this feature is not essential, as just as attractive a pool may be built on a flat piece of ground. In this instance a sloping background should be given to the flat ground for proper effect.

The size of the basin and the shape are matters which must be decided upon to suit the convenience of the owner. The little pool on page 175 is twelve feet long and six feet wide at its widest part, with an irregular boundary. Such a naturalistic style of planting as the one illustrated gives the best opportunity for the use of plant materials and is generally favored for small grounds.

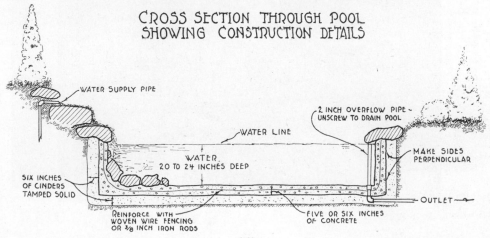

CROSS SECTION THROUGH POOL
SHOWING CONSTRUCTION DETAILS

WATER SUPPLY PIPE

2 INCH OVERFLOW PIPE
UNSCREW TO DRAIN POOL

WATER LINE

WATER
20 TO 24 INCHES DEEP

MAKE SIDES
PERPENDICULAR

SIX INCHES
OF CINDERS
TAMPED SOLID

OUTLET

REINFORCE WITH
WOVEN WIRE FENCING
OR 3/8 INCH IRON RODS

FIVE OR SIX INCHES
OF CONCRETE

This pool is constructed so that no concrete shows. Porous rocks over-hang the edge of the water so that the water covers half of the rocks. This gives a moss covered edge and more of a natural and pleasing appearance.

Much of the enjoyment comes from building the pool, and while it requires a little painstaking effort, almost anyone with a little help can build a small pool. After the site has been selected, small stakes can be used to outline the general shape of the pool. Excavating can then be done, digging down two feet or two and one-half feet. Coarse gravel or cinders should then be thrown in the hole and evenly distributed to a depth of about six inches. This should be firmly tamped to form the base for the concrete. In climates where there is considerable frost, we recommend laying a piece of rather heavy woven-wire fence, or iron rods, or some other reinforcement in the concrete which will help prevent cracking or damage from severe freezing and thawing.

Before mixing the concrete, all outlets and drains must be provided for as shown in sketch, and you should make certain that the various edges of the pool are level. If one edge is too low, the water will run out, of course, before the pool is full. An easy way to insure level edges is to drive stakes at various points at the edge of the pool. With an ordinary carpenter's spirit level on a

In this pool the builder has succeeded very well in making it look natural. Various grasses, reeds, and swampy plants combined with Evergreens give this pool the appearance of being created by nature.

This pool is intended as a display for water plants but the owner has very wisely taken advantage of the formal growing habit of the Redcedars to mark the four corners of the pool.

straight edged board, establish the correct level and mark it on the stakes. Then you are ready to mix and lay the concrete.

The following proportions in the mixing of concrete will be found entirely satisfactory for making a pool. One part cement, two and one-half parts sand, and five parts gravel. For an extra-nice finish which will make the pool water-proof, a top dressing of one part cement and two or three parts sand will give a fine finish.

In formal pools such as this one, the use of stratified rocks laid in regular formation forms the outline of the pool. A pair of Scotch Pines has been added. Other Evergreens could also be used here.

Thorough mixing is very important in concrete work. If the cement shows in streaks, the mixing has not been well done. Do not mix a larger batch than can be quickly put into the forms.

Sometimes a very naturalistic effect can be carried out by embedding stones or coarse gravel loosely in the concrete, after it is laid, to take away the artificial appearance.

SOME SUGGESTIONS FOR MAKING ROCK GARDENS

You may use a regular edging of flat or stratified stones, which may be embedded in the concrete before it hardens, or the surface may be left entirely smooth. Or it may be decorated with small boulders of whatever type is easiest to obtain in your neighborhood.

Many suggestions for the use of rock plants, building of pockets for alpines, as well as information on how to raise lilies and water plants, can be obtained from nurserymen who specialize in aquatic and perennial plants. The suggestions which we make here apply only to the use of Evergreen trees which should make the framework or background around the pool and rockery. Flowers and plants can be filled in as space permits.

The artistic and natural appearance of a rock garden and pool is something which you cannot gain from reading books or suggestions. The artistic effect which you may have admired in other pools will furnish an outline for you to follow. The rocks, the trees and plant materials, as well as the location, and your own artistic sense will govern your results.

In many ways, pools of this kind making use of large massive rocks give a closer approach to the natural rock formations. The only difficulty, of course, is in obtaining and moving the rocks. Where facilities for doing this are available large rocks are usually to be desired.

The use of water adds much to the enjoyment of home grounds.

Some of the chief faults in rockeries made by beginners are too much stone and too great regularity. It is better to have a few larger stones than many small ones. The larger you can get the rocks the better for the appearance of your rockery. Broken rocks, pieces of concrete, and other unnatural looking objects should never be used. Stones which are rather porous make more interesting subjects than hard boulders. If the porous stones are set so the lower half of each stone is touching the water, they will quickly become covered with moss. Porous stones full of holes and depressions also give opportunity for planting many delicate plants. Round, water-worn boulders are difficult to place to look properly, while egg-shaped rocks are not of much use. The use of slab-like rocks is equally to be avoided.

Evergreens furnish a background of beautiful green foliage for the rockery or pool. Even on a small scale, a few tall-growing trees are necessary to give height and mass to the background of the planting. Interesting low and dwarf forms can be used around the edge of the pool and among the rocks.

For overhanging rocks, and overhanging the edge of the pool, there are a number of strictly creeping Evergreens among the Junipers: Waukegan Juniper, Bar Harbor Juniper, Japanese Juniper, and Sargent Juniper. The Andorra Juniper might also be included in this group. For planting among the rocks, there are others of a dwarf habit but slightly more upright in growth, such as Savin Juniper, Pfitzer Juniper, Prostrate Juniper, Koster Juniper, Meyer Juniper, Dwarf Alberta Spruce, Mugho Pine, Japanese Table Pine, and Dwarf Japanese Yew. For the background of the pool or at its border as a frame to the planting, almost any of the taller varieties of Evergreens will prove suitable.

Arrange the planting so that the roots of the trees will not dry out. Do not expect Evergreens to grow in soil too dry or shallow.

Naturalistic Pool

Planting Sketch for Picture on Opposite Page

This pool, built of concrete, is six feet wide at its widest point, and about twelve feet long. It is largely planted with Evergreens in variety as indicated by the following planting key. Not all of the trees are shown in the picture, and of course the planting could be greatly simplified, and the cost could be reduced by using fewer trees and smaller sizes.

Alpine plants, perennials and annuals are not shown but are easily obtainable and are also necessary to complete the planting.

Key for sketch shown below:

1. *Woodward Arborvitae.*
2. *White Spruce.*
3. *White Spruce.*
4. *Sargent Juniper.*
5. *Black Hill Spruce.*
6. *Norway Spruce.*
7. *Cannart Redcedar.*
8. *White Spruce.*
9. *Savin Juniper.*
10. *Japanese Juniper.*
11. *Redcedar.*
12. *Dundee Juniper.*
13. *White Pine.*
14. *Savin Juniper.*
15. *Cannart Juniper.*
16. *White Pine (not in picture).*
17. *Pfitzer Juniper (not in picture).*
18. *Japanese Juniper.*
19. *Sargent Juniper.*
20. *Woodward Arborvitae.*

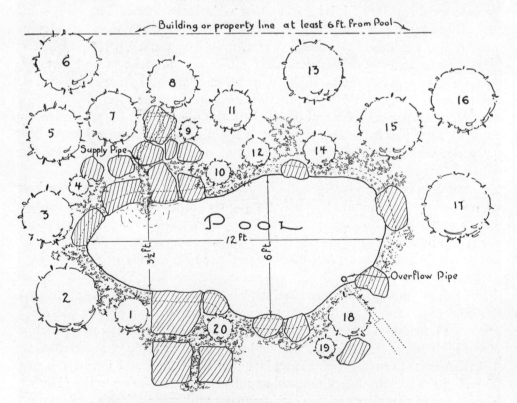

GROUND PLAN ~ SHOWING
LOCATION of EVERGREENS and SIZE of POOL

The ground plan and list of material used in this planting is shown on opposite page.

POOL AND ROCK GARDEN

This garden is on the grounds of Mr. and Mrs. A. H. Hill, Dundee, Illinois. Tall Evergreens used as a background are various Spruces, Pines, and Junipers. Among the rocks and along the edge of the pool, are many forms of creeping Juniper, including Andorra Juniper, Japanese Juniper, Sargent Juniper, Bar Harbor Juniper and Waukegan Juniper.

In the semi-upright varieties are Pfitzer Juniper, Savin Juniper, Von Ehron Juniper, Meyer Juniper, Spiny Greek Juniper, Golden Prostrate Juniper, Mugho Pine, Koster Juniper, several kinds of Dwarf Spruces and various Yews. There are, of course, many perennial rock plants and an assortment of water plants to add interest. The bridge leads to a flower garden further on.

Some of the brighter-colored Evergreens, such as the bright Golden Prostrate Juniper, Goldtip Redcedar and trees of unusual color, have an interesting place in plantings of this kind.

FREQUENT PRUNING NECESSARY

Frequent trimming of plants and trees used in rockeries and around pools makes it possible to use a much wider variety and keep trees small and within bounds for many years.

Chapter XXXV

Garden-Lighting

T HE enjoyment of a garden may be greatly extended by effective lighting of certain portions. Most of us do not have the leisure time to spend in our gardens during the daytime, and with modern lighting equipment some very startling and beautiful effects may easily be created.

Lighting, of course, must be concealed so as to avoid any lights too glaring or too bright. Flood-lighting does not give the inviting and attractive effect which may be obtained from lights placed on the ground with suitable reflectors to reflect the light upwards. Some effects thus obtained will be noticed from the two pictures shown on this page.

Anyone interested in carrying out similar effects may secure the cooperation of his local electric light company. Most concerns of this kind employ electrical lighting engineers, able to furnish and install the necessary equipment.

Newly-constructed grounds should include wiring installed under ground, but older grounds may also be lighted with a little extra work.

CHAPTER XXXVI

Evergreen Windbreaks

THE comforting influence of an Evergreen windbreak can scarcely be realized unless you have stepped behind a row of sturdy Evergreens on a blustering winter's day. In farming sections, especially in the prairie states, the Evergreen windbreak has long been recognized as an important factor in protecting the home, stock and buildings.

In selecting Evergreens for windbreaks, we must choose strong, upright growers, which develop into thick and compact trees—varieties which retain their lower branches to the ground. Most widely used in the farming sections is the Norway Spruce. Other good windbreak Evergreens are White Spruce, Colorado Blue Spruce, Austrian Pine and Douglas Fir. When planted close together, the Redcedar and American Arborvitae are also recommended.

DIRECTIONS FOR PLANTING WINDBREAKS

In planting trees for windbreaks, success depends to a great extent upon the preparation of the ground to receive them. It should be carefully plowed or spaded as deeply as possible.

Three rows of trees make a very satisfactory windbreak. Plant the extra tall,

A farm home before it was given the protection of an Evergreen Windbreak—at the whim of the blizzard winds, bleak, "cold as an abandoned barn."

The same farm home after being given the blanket-like protection of an Evergreen Windbreak—warm, free from sweep of wind, worth hundreds of dollars more to owner or buyer.

fast-growing varieties (Pines), in the row forming the outside; medium-growers (Spruce), in the middle row, with the low-growing trees (Arborvitae and Cedars), to form the inside row. Allow at least ten feet between the trees and between the rows.

As shown in the picture above, a single row makes a very serviceable windbreak. When planted in a single row, set the trees about ten feet apart. Windbreaks, of course, should be planted so as to protect from the prevailing winter winds.

Hoe or cultivate thoroughly the first few summers after planting, especially during June, July and August. Water generously at frequent intervals during summer.

Figure 1. The low hedge for bordering walks and beds.

CHAPTER XXXVII

Evergreen Hedges

AS illustrated in this chapter, hedges may be tall or low, close-clipped or natural, depending upon the purpose they serve.

In the earliest beginnings of landscape development, hedges were used, often in intricate designs. In England, where privacy is demanded at all costs, the hedge often becomes the main feature of the landscape plan.

Hedges serve several distinct and important uses in landscaping. The dwarf hedge, maintained closely clipped at a height of only a few inches, may be used as a border for flower beds, or to line a garden walk. See figure 1. For this purpose we must start with small plants set closely together, only six or eight inches apart. Where the climate permits, the Dwarf Boxwood is ideal for the dwarf hedge. Small seedlings of Redcedar or Chinese Juniper make suit-

Figure 2. The medium sized hedge of Arborvitae for lot lines.

Figure 3. A close clipped Hemlock hedge.

able low hedges when frequently trimmed and when the hedge is in the full sun. There are also some good forms of Dwarf Arborvitae; the Little Gem and the Tom Thumb varieties are sometimes used. Best of all is the Dwarf Japanese Yew, if we start with little trees only six to ten inches high. The Yew hedge has the distinct advantage of a rich deep green color and also the ability to withstand considerable shade.

Hedges may also be used for borders to take the place of fences along lot lines and, if in keeping with the landscape plan, as a border along the street

Figure 4. A slightly trimmed informal hedge of Norway Spruce.

Figure 5.   A perfect Yew hedge in an old English garden.

walk. The American Arborvitae, the Pyramidal Arborvitae, the Hemlock, the Japanese Yew, the Norway Spruce, and even the Douglas Fir, may be used for such a hedge. The Arborvitae seems to be a favorite, in the northern states at least. If space permits, set the trees in a double row, spacing the trees eighteen inches apart, and the rows eighteen to twenty-four inches apart. Allow plenty of room for the hedge to grow, setting it at least three feet from lot lines and

Figure 6.   American Arborvitae maintained as a high hedge.

sidewalks. Such hedges should be maintained at the proper height, which may be anywhere from three feet tall to perhaps six feet or more, to suit their purpose. See figure 6.

Other uses for hedges are: to afford privacy, to keep out intruders, or to form a background for some garden feature, such as a statue, a fountain, or a garden house. Such hedges may be closely clipped, as shown in figures 2, 3 and 5, or allow to grow in a less formal manner, as shown in figure 4. For this type of hedge the same trees may be used as are mentioned in the preceding paragraph. Hedges of this sort may be kept at a height of six or eight feet, depending upon the circumstances of what purpose they serve.

The time for planting hedges is the same as for other Evergreens. Detailed suggestions are given elsewhere in this book on the subject of proper planting, fertilizing, culture and pruning of Evergreens.

The question of how long it takes to grow a hedge, depends upon what tree is being used, how it is cared for, and how tall it is to be. Perfect hedges are not grown in a single year. Four or five years should begin to make an attractive Evergreen hedge. When once established and given careful attention, an Evergreen hedge will be a source of pride to the owner for a lifetime.

It must not be assumed that the various Evergreens mentioned are the *only* ones that are suitable for hedges. In more temperate climates there are many other varieties of Evergreens well suited for use as hedges. The trees which we have mentioned are all suitable for planters in northern Illinois and localities of similar climate.

A combination of Spruce and Mugho Pine using two rows.

Chapter XXXVIII

Evergreens for Window-Boxes

THERE is no need for window-boxes to be bare of decoration during the winter months. When the early frosts in the fall kill the flowers and tender plants, then is the time to put in refreshing green trees. Various artistic arrangements of Evergreens can be made. A single row of

A single row of Evergreens may be used. In this case Pyramidal Arborvitae have been selected.

184

Pyramidal Arborvitae, or, in fact, any shapely green tree which may be available may be used, as shown in the picture at bottom of page 184.

If you prefer a massed arrangement of different colors and texture of foliage, the arrangement as pictured at top of page 184, is a suggestion. In this planting, Norway Spruce is used with a second row of Mugho Pine in front.

A tall tree at each end, with low trees in the middle, fits the need of some windows. It makes some difference, of course, whether the box is level with the window sill or set slightly below it, as to what size of trees to use. Plantings for some windows need to be kept low; or, if it is a second floor window, larger trees may be used. Small trees 10 to 12, 12 to 18, or 18 to 24 inches are the sizes most often planted for window-boxes. The deeper the box, the better chance the trees have to keep in a fresh, live condition. Boxes should be at least 8 inches deep to accommodate the roots. Plant in good, black soil and keep well-watered until the ground freezes. If the box is exposed to the south where it is very sunny, an occasional watering during the winter will be necessary.

Most people prefer to remove the trees in the spring and replace with flowers. However, by careful attention to watering and feeding, it is possible to keep the trees from year to year.

For the small cost involved, nothing can give more winter cheer than winter window boxes. They are attractive from the house, looking out, as well as a joy to passersby.

Evergreens for Use in Tubs

For entrances, balconies, and other decorative purposes, around homes, clubs, hotels, tea rooms, stores, etc., Evergreens in tubs are cheerful and inviting. Any shapely tree of good, green winter color may be used for this purpose. Arborvitaes and Junipers are better suited to the purpose than coarser Spruces, Firs, and Pines. Plant in good soil in a tub large enough to accommodate the roots. Tubs should be from fourteen to sixteen inches deep for small trees, 3 to 4 feet tall.

Frequent watering, except during severe freezing weather, is all the attention needed.

Pyramidal Arborvitae

CHAPTER XXXIX

Evergreens for Use in the Cemetery

"Yet strew
Upon my grave
Such offerings as you have,
Forsaken cypresse and sad Ewe,
For kinder flowers can take no birth
Or growth from such unhappy Earth."

NEARLY three hundred years ago an English poet thus refers to the feeling commonly held at that period towards Evergreens.

The most likely reason why the Yew was extensively planted in the early churchyards in England was the fact that branches of the Yew were carried in processions on various church days, in keeping with the earlier practice of Christians who performed certain of their ceremonies with the palm.

Something of the Old World association between Evergreens and cemeteries did descend to America in past generations. This fact, more than anything else, no doubt, has accounted for the feeling that many persons have had that "Evergreens remind them of the cemetery." To this day, throughout the rural sections, particularly in the great Middle West, Norway Spruce are prominent in many of the older cemeteries.

About one hundred years ago, in 1831 to be exact, Mount Auburn Cemetery near Boston was laid out. Up to that time it had been the custom to locate cemeteries adjacent to churches and to arrange them in symmetrical squares with monuments closely crowded together. With the advent of the Mount Auburn development it became the custom to seek a location for a cemetery far-removed from the Village or City where its landscape development might be carried on in the manner of a park with winding drives and beautiful groups of trees and shrubs. In almost every locality cemeteries of this type of design are now found. In this newer style of landscaping, Evergreens are extensively used. They lend a touch of color to the otherwise bleak winter landscape, and in the minds of many people they symbolize perpetual memory.

It is not our purpose to make suggestions for the laying out of a new cemetery. This is a matter which, of course, needs the professional services of a landscape architect skilled in cemetery design.

There are, however, many persons who wish to plant Evergreens on their own cemetery lots, and it is for these persons that we will try to give some practical suggestions.

A type of planting typical of modern cemetery design.

One should first determine what regulations exist concerning the planting of Evergreens, or any trees in fact, in a cemetery before planting is commenced. Many cemetery officials reserve the right to regulate the planting, so as to avoid any type of planting which might disturb the beauty of the whole. A great many cemeteries also have their own nursery and will gladly cooperate with lot owners in choosing the trees and also in taking care of the planting and maintenance.

There can, of course, be no set plan of planting because of the many various conditions, such as the size of the lot, the location of any markers or monuments, condition of shade, and future need of space for burials. A few general rules might be laid down, however. We should choose varieties, for the most part, which are known to be long lived, and which are easily cared for. Many times lot-owners live at a great distance and cannot give this planting attention which they normally would give to any planting. We must also bear in mind the need of choosing trees which will remain small. We should not plant those which eventually will develop into gigantic specimens overcoming and overshadowing the entire lot.

On the ordinary cemetery lot there are but two or three types of plantings which can usually be made. Markers at each corner of the lot are often used. These trees should be set two feet or more in from the corner of the lot and may consist of one tree or a triangular planting of three trees. For such a style of planting we must choose trees which are of a small-growing habit or those which may easily be maintained in close quarters. Various types of Junipers, Yews and Arborvitae, as well as other dwarf forms of Pines and Spruces are best suited for plantings of this kind.

There is, of course, opportunity for using Evergreens to furnish a suitable background or outline for a monument. Such a planting should not be of such proportion that it overshadows the monument but rather of such design that it softens the lines of the monument and places it in a more natural setting. We show a picture of such a planting which is made up of one Pyramidal Arborvitae, two Hemlock, and four Pfitzer Juniper. Because of the great variation in design of monuments, the actual trees to be used for this purpose are a matter which cannot be definitely recommended without considering the actual monument and its location on the lot.

The third use to which Evergreens may be put in cemeteries is for grave covering. There is a small Evergreen plant known as Japanese Spurge (Pachysandra) which is frequently used for this purpose. However, it requires a shaded location for satisfactory results. Where the graves are in the open sun, there are a number of forms of dwarf, creeping Junipers which are suitable, including such well known sorts as Japanese Juniper, Sargent Juniper, Waukegan Juniper, Bar Harbor Juniper, and others.

In conclusion we may say that modern use of Evergreens in the cemetery bears no relation whatever to the old conception of Evergreen trees as we find them in the older cemeteries. We should choose Evergreens in keeping with the special conditions of each lot and should always keep in mind our purpose, which is to create beauty and to give a natural, park-like appearance.

Evergreens properly selected furnish an ideal setting for cemetery memorials.

CHAPTER XL

A Word for Reforestation

WE quote some astonishing statistics on the forest situation in the United States, from a publication of the "Institute of Forest Genetics," Placerville, Calif.: "Four-fifths of the Nation's timberlands, or 370,000,000 acres, is in the hands of private owners. . . . Meanwhile the national timber supply is being consumed more than three times as fast as it is being replaced by new growth. Less than one-sixth remains of the virgin forests that once covered more than half of the total land area of the United States. This remnant is being called upon to supply the great bulk of the 25,000,000,000 cubic feet of wood cut each year to meet the needs of the world's greatest wood-using country. Present over-production of *lumber* makes it difficult to realize that the Nation is approaching a *timber* shortage; but even now there exist serious regional shortages, and in sections of the country that only a few decades ago ranked high in lumber production."

The growing of trees as a profitable crop is a practice that has been followed for many years by the federal government and the various states. Large, privately-owned industries with far-seeing management, and individuals with wastelands have been carrying on systematic reforestation in increasing numbers. Aside from the actual profit to be gained, reforesting has a much greater economic aspect. Many organizations and prominent men have devoted cease-

| A. | B. | C. |

A simple method of planting. "a" making a hole with grub hoe, "b" setting the tree, "c" firming the soil around the tree. Photographs courtesy of Wisconsin Conservation Department.

less effort for years past to arouse public interest in the preservation and systematic use of existing forests, and the planting of trees for future generations.

European countries much older than ours in point of settlement have stringent laws relating to the cutting of trees and the planting of new forests.

Trees for forest planting are available at a most reasonable cost when used in large quantities, and, even in small plantings, the expense is small.

Lands unsuited to any other use generally are made to produce trees. Worn-out, agricultural lands, sand dunes and barrens, and cut-over timber lands offer fine opportunities for forest planting. Planting the water-sheds to conserve the nation's water supply is increasingly receiving the attention of municipalities. Owners of private estates and farms can leave no finer heritage of more genuine worth to their successors.

The actual work of planting is simple and can be done readily by anyone. The planting is best done by two men, one with a grub hoe to make holes, and the other with a pail of trees. The trees should be set about six feet apart each way, which will require about 1,200 trees per acre.

Preparation of the soil is not necessary, but the plantation must be protected from fire and grazing must be prohibited. In five to ten years, or before, if possible, the brush, weeds, and rubbish should be cut out, but further attention is not necessary until the trees have reached twenty years of age. Thinning and any trimming will have to be looked after, depending upon the soil conditions, the rate of growth, and the varieties being grown.

Ten year old White Pine (left), ten year old Norway Pine (right) Douglas County, Wisconsin.
Photograph courtesy of Wisconsin Conservation Department.

CHAPTER XLI

Profits in Raising Christmas Trees

IT is estimated that five million Christmas Trees are used in the United States every year. The use of Christmas Trees is a well-established custom of all nationalities in every section of the country.

Government bulletin (No. 1453) says, "High prices appear likely to prevail in the future, and, in consequence, growing Christmas Trees in plantations near the large consuming centers is an attractive business proposition. This is particularly true for centers in the Eastern and Middle Western states which are rather distant from a natural source of supply. In a plantation adjacent to a good public road, it seems probable that all trees could be sold right on the ground to people passing in automobiles."

PREFERENCE FOR HOME GROWN TREES

There is a growing preference for Christmas Trees which have been produced locally. There are several reasons for this. One reason, probably the most important, is the fact that the trees retain their foliage throughout the holiday season. They are usually cut a week or so before Christmas and if kept in a cool place will not shed their needles even though brought into a warm house and left for a week or ten days.

On the other hand, the wild trees from the swamps are cut during October, tied tightly together in bundles, and stacked up ready for shipment. They are

A young Christmas Tree Planting—making use of waste space in a new orchard.

usually cut two months before being used, and for this reason are, many times, almost useless when they are set up in the home.

There is also a great advantage with the home-grown trees in the general shape and character of the trees. Those produced at home have a thriftier appearance and are of much better shape. This is a big point because the trade demands a shapely tree and is willing to pay for it.

It is also true that there is much agitation among various State Horticultural Boards and Entomologists to prohibit wild trees' being shipped in. This is done as a protective measure against plant diseases. In the woods where the wild trees are produced, plant diseases are sometimes prevalent, and it has been shown that serious pests have been spread from Christmas Trees brought in from the woods. Some quarantines are already in effect.

The variety most in demand, and which is recommended by authorities on the subject, is the Norway Spruce. The Norway Spruce grows fast and makes a shapely and compact growth, and has a bright green color.

Trees usually planted, are seedlings or small, transplanted sizes which can be planted out directly into rows. If cultivated the first year or two, they will quickly become established.

Different planting distances are used, depending upon the plan of marketing. For instance, if the trees are set three feet apart each way, about 5,000 trees should be used per acre. On this basis the plan would be to cut out every other tree as soon as they start to touch (in about two or three years). This would give you a crop of trees ranging from one foot up to one and one-half feet.

There is a good market for these small trees, especially for table use. Small holders or pots can be sold with the trees. If the trees are decorated with a little tinsel and properly displayed in some store window, they will bring a good price.

Many people prefer a tree dug with ball of earth which can be planted in the ground after the holidays. Orders for such trees must be taken before the ground freezes.

After small trees are removed, the rest of the trees can develop for two or three years longer, at which time some trees will run three feet and some four feet in height. Of course, the market will take some trees up to six feet, seven feet, and eight feet.

An acre of Christmas Trees in five to seven years' time, property managed, should net a profit of at least $3,000.00, and with practically no work, except the original small cost of planting the trees.

In a government Farmers' Bulletin (No. 1453), the following suggestions are given for planting: "Christmas Trees should be given more care than the ordinary forest plantation. The trees should be set out on land prepared by plowing as for any field crop. After the trees are planted, they should be cultivated for two or three years in the same way that corn is cultivated. Since the trees will be grown for only five to eight years, and in no case perhaps over ten years after they are set out, they can be planted at the rate of about 5,000 per acre. A triangular spacing of three by three feet will mean about 5,000 per acre.

The trees will not all grow at a uniform rate. It will be possible to harvest some in four or five years after planting, and others in each succeeding year. Excessively rapid growth should not be sought, for slower-growing trees are more compact and better-liked for Christmas Tree use. The season for planting is during April or early May in the North Central States.

There is also a good market for table Christmas Trees for small homes and apartments.

PART IV
Description of Varieties

Chapter XLII

Firs (Abies)

THE family of Firs is of great value in landscaping. They have a symmetrical, shapely form, and, when properly selected for their site, they are long-lived. In old age they develop into majestic subjects.

The localities of the world which produce most of the Firs are the Cascade Mountains of Oregon and Washington, the Rocky Mountains, particularly in Colorado, Japan, and some countries along the Mediterranean Sea.

As will be found by referring to pages 43 and 44, there are approximately thirty species of Fir in cultivation. In addition, there are probably an equal number of horticultural varieties, although the Firs have not produced as many horticultural variations as some of the other families of Evergreens.

It is a characteristic of most Firs that they require a moist, but well drained soil, and that they thrive better in a humid climate. For this reason the beautiful and immense Firs of the far northwest, such as the Silver Fir, Cascade Fir, Great Silver Fir, and the Red Fir are not suited to planting in the middle west, the northern, and the southern states. Likewise, many of the interesting Japanese Firs, such as the Nikko Fir, the Veitch Fir, and the Sackhalin Fir, are not permanently satisfactory in the great central area of the United States.

The Nordman Fir, from the Caucasus Mountains, the Greek Fir, or the Algerian, or Pinsapo, the Spanish Fir, are of little value in that part of the United States subject to severe cold, or drying winds, or extreme heat.

While we cannot recommend many of these Firs for our own use, we do not wish to discount the beauty of these trees, or to intimate that they are not to be made use of. In England and other parts of Europe, they are considered among the finest of Evergreens, and in other localities where there is humid climate they may be freely used.

It may appear, therefore, that the selection of Firs is very limited as far as planters in the middle west states are concerned. There are, however, several Firs which we will describe, and of which we will show a number of pictures in the following pages.

We have included among the Firs, the Douglas Fir. While this tree is not properly of the same family as the rest of the Firs, it is commonly called a Fir. Because of peculiar botanical differences the Douglas Fir is given the name *Pseudotsuga,* while other Firs of the true Fir family belong to the *Abies* group.

195

CONCOLOR FIR

Concolor or White Fir
(Abies Concolor)

By far the most outstanding Fir, because of its ability to withstand severe winter conditions, is the Concolor, or White Fir. Some confusion exists with reference to this tree, from the fact that the type of Concolor Fir which is found in the Pacific Coast Mountain area, while it goes by the same name as the Rocky Mountain tree, is, in reality, distinguished in many ways from its near relative, the Concolor Fir of the Rocky Mountain area. Most references which are found to the Concolor Fir, particularly as it is planted in European countries, concerns the Concolor Fir of the Pacific Coast range, rather than the Colorado family. While the Concolor Fir grows in its native range over a considerable north and south area in the Rocky Mountains, trees of the most desirable habit, color, and hardiness come from Colorado.

These trees are widely recommended by all writers on Evergreens as the one Fir best-suited to withstand conditions of heat and drought and are generally the most satisfactory of all Firs.

There is some variation in the color and the foliage of the Concolor Fir. Many trees are of a decidedly bluish color; others are green. All, however, run toward a slightly glaucous tint. In ultimate developments there is wide variation in what may be expected of this tree. In forest conditions, when planted close together, it reaches to a considerable height, but trees planted in ornamental plantings generally do not reach more than fifty or sixty feet, with a considerable spread of branches, perhaps as much as ten to twelve feet. When small, these trees have a tendency to grow rather irregular and for a few years do not make a symmetrical, even growth. When fully established, however, they carry a beautiful, even spread of branches and are one of the most beautiful of all Evergreens of this type.

This detailed picture shows the foliage of Concolor Fir, approximately one-half natural size.

On the opposite page is a picture in natural colors of a specimen of Concolor Fir photographed at Dundee, Illinois. This tree was approximately nine feet in height. It has had some trimming, in order to produce a compact growth. The color is slightly more bluish than most Concolor Fir. The correct color is more nearly as shown in the small foliage picture to the right.

Cork or Arizona Fir

CORK OR ARIZONA FIR
(Abies arizonica)

This tree gets its name from its very whitish, almost pure cork bark. In color it is one of the bluest of the Firs, rivaling the Blue Spruce. The underside of the needles is extremely whitish, or pale blue in color. It grows rather slowly and makes a narrow pyramid of unusual shapliness.

Its native home is in a small area in the Francisco Mountains, in northwest Arizona, a locality where it is said that frost occurs every month in the year. For this reason, the Cork Fir is better suited to climatic conditions in the middle west than most of the other Firs.

VEITCH FIR
(Abies Veitchi)

This tree is native to high elevation in the Mountains of Central Japan. It makes a rather slender, upright, symmetrical tree, ultimately reaching sixty feet, sometimes a great deal more. The foliage is shiny and waxy, bright grass green above, whitish beneath. It was named in honor of John Gould Veitch, who brought the tree to England about 1860. It is typical in appearance with many of the other Japanese Firs. This tree is not well suited to the central west, but may succeed under protected conditions. It does well in many of the eastern states where humidity is greater.

Veitch Fir

Balsam Fir

FRASER FIR
(Abies Fraseri)

This is a tree quite similar to Balsam Fir, often called southern Balsam Fir. It grows in a wild state in the Allegheny Mountains, extending into North Carolina and Tennessee. It has the characteristic shiny, green foliage, whitish beneath. Because it is accustomed to elevation of around 5000 feet, it is quite hardy and usually is considered more satisfactory than the Balsam Fir. This is a picture of a specimen about four feet high, growing at Dundee, Illinois. The tree is now about ten feet in height and in an excellent condition. Like the Balsam Fir it has a very pungent odor. It has attractive purplish cones.

BALSAM FIR
(Abies balsamea)

This Fir is doubtless more familiar to residents of the central west than any other, for the reason that it is the only Fir which is found, in the native state, in the coniferous forests of Michigan, Minnesota, and Wisconsin. It inhabits swampy grounds, but is sometimes found on hillsides. It is not a large growing tree, but is very attractive when small. It has the characteristic shiny, bright-green foliage, whitish beneath. The needles are very fragrant. Unfortunately it is but short-lived in cultivation, except when planted in a moist, cool location. It is not recommended for a permanent tree. Its habit of growth is typically pyramid of medium spread.

Fraser Fir

Douglas Fir

Douglas Fir
(Pseudotsuga douglasi)

More Douglas Firs are doubtless planted than any other Fir. It is a tree which does exceptionally well over a large part of the United States, except in the extreme south.

It is a tree with an interesting history. It forms the leading lumber tree of the western part of the United States and is extremely valuable in this respect. At the same time, it is an outstanding tree for ornamental use.

Like the Concolor Fir which extends over a wide area, there are two separate and distinct types existing. Not all botanists recognize this distinction, but the two types bear little resemblance to each other. The gigantic-growing Douglas Fir, some specimens of which are shown in the illustration at the bottom of this page, extend over considerable range in the northwest Pacific Coast area. These trees are of tremendous size and require the humid climate and the less extreme conditions of weather which prevail in that locality. The other type of Douglas Fir, which is the one pictured on the opposite page, is the Rocky Mountain tree, extending over a considerable area north and south from Montana to New Mexico. Within this range are also many variations of type. Those trees which are native to Montana are greatly different in appearance, in rapidity of growth, than those trees from Colorado. The trees from the southern range are less desirable, both in their habit of growth and in their hardiness. Either the so-called Snowy Mountain type, a slower growing, shorter leaf form,

which is native of the Snowy Mountain range in central Montana, or the Colorado form are perfectly dependable, widely used and appreciated for ornamental subjects.

The Rocky Mountain type, which is the only one that concerns planters in the great central west, grows to much less size than the Pacific coast type, although it is not uncommon

These gigantic trees measure from ten to twelve feet in diameter and are preserved in Rainier National Park in the State of Washington. Such specimens as these, known nowhere else in the world, naturally created an intense interest in the tree life of the great northwest when first discovered more than one hundred years ago. (Photograph furnished through the courtesy of Rainier National Park Company.)

Specimen shown in colored photograph on opposite page was taken at Dundee, Illinois.

to find an old specimen sixty feet or more, with a spread of branches up to twelve feet in diameter. The tree has a very commendable habit of retaining its lower limbs in old age, which attribute greatly adds to its beauty.

There is considerable variation in the color of the foliage. Many trees are soft blue in color. Frequently, horticultural varieties are grown by which this characteristic is insured. When produced from seeds, however, only a small number are of bluish color; the others range from light to dark green.

It is a rapid grower and has long, graceful branches, less stiff than the Spruce. The foliage is not sharp and stiff, but soft, flexible, and also fragrant. It seems to thrive under conditions of shade better than most trees of this type and will stand considerable crowding.

This tree is named in honor of David Douglas, a young Scotchman, who made his way in 1825 to Vancouver, under the auspices of the Royal Horticultural Society of London. He spent two years gathering new plants from that rich source of tree and plant life and, upon his return to England two years later, introduced 165 plants which were new to Europe. While he was not the first to discover this magnificent tree, it having been previously found by Menzies, he was the first explorer who succeeded in gathering seeds, and the tree was named in his honor. David Douglas later returned to the Pacific northwest, as he was greatly fascinated with the remarkable vegetation in that locality. In coming home from this second voyage, he stopped at the Islands of Hawaii, and there, by an unfortunate accident, fell into a pit which was designed as a trap for wild cattle, and there he was gored to death by a bull. Although he lived only to the age of thirty-three, he made for himself a name which lives in Horticultural Annals. There is scarcely a garden in European countries which does not at least contain some plant or tree which David Douglas found and brought home from his extended journey.

Anyone who may wish to make a more thorough study of the Douglas Fir and

David Douglas

to realize the high regard in which this tree has been held in Great Britain, should refer to that remarkable work, *Pinetum Britannicum* published in England in 1884. These volumes, which are 22 x 16 inches in size, devote twenty-two pages to the Douglas Fir, including two color plates and thirty illustrations.

The value of Douglas Fir as an ornamental tree can hardly be overstated. It is regarded by many people as the outstanding tree of its type for planters in the middle western states.

CEDARS (Cedrus)

The true Cedar family is composed of a small group of three species, native to the Mediterranean region, the Himalayas, and northern Africa. None of these trees are hardy in the north central states, although they are prominently used throughout the south, where they replace many of the Firs and Spruces of northern plantings. They are also hardy in the eastern states, occasionally being seen as far north as New England.

DEODAR CEDAR (Cedrus deodara)

This is an upright growing tree with graceful, drooping branches. Its foliage is pale bluish in color; it grows rapidly and develops a beautiful outline as it reaches old age. This is a tree highly regarded in India where it is called "Tree of the Gods."

Deodar Cedar

ATLAS CEDAR (Cedrus atlantica)

The horticultural variety most commonly planted is the variety Glauca, which has very blue foliage. The specimen shown in this photograph is a newly-planted one, not as bushy and compact as older trees.

CEDAR OF LEBANON (Cedrus libani)

Because of frequent biblical reference to this tree, it is widely known, at least by name. It is less planted, however, than the other types of Cedrus. It reaches a great size up to one hundred feet, with massive trunk and top. A photograph of some of the trees on Mt. Lebanon will be found on page 8.

Atlas Cedar

CHAPTER XLIII

False Cypress (Chamaecyparis)

THIS extensive group of Evergreens includes many which are commonly known as Cypress and Retinospora. The true Cypress, however, are known by the name of *Cupressus,* and the old name of *Retinospora,* which is still very widely used, does not officially exist.

Trees of this group are of extremely variable habit, which fact accounts for the large number of horticultural varieties which have been propagated during the past one hundred years. Many of the Evergreen nurseries of Europe have introduced variations of the Chamaecyparis. A list of the important varieties of this extensive family is given on page 46 of this book.

Because of the fact that these trees are not universally hardy, we have not described or illustrated them extensively. In the vicinity of Chicago, as well as all the territory lying west and north, these trees are not suitable for the climate. They are, however, great favorites as far north as St. Louis, Cincinnati, and points of similar latitude, as well as in other districts where there is not the intensity of severe, winter cold. They are important trees throughout the southern states and are also extensively planted in the eastern part of the country.

Lawson Cypress

LAWSON CYPRESS
(Chamaecyparis lawsoniana)

It will be noted from the list of varieties given on page 46 of this book, that there are numerous forms of this interesting tree, having variations of color and growing habit. The tree which is shown in the colored illustration is the seedling type from which the various horticultural varieties have been selected.

Hinoki Cypress

Hinoki Cypress
(Chamaecyparis obtusa)

This species has also produced a large number of horticultural varieties of various peculiarities of foliage and growth. All of them are of small stature, and may be easily trimmed and maintained in a small size. It is a tree native to Japan, in which country it has been highly regarded for many years, a number of its unusual horticultural forms having originated there.

Space does not permit us to include an extensive description or illustration of this family, but two of the most interesting of the horticultural forms are shown.

The species from which the horticultural varieties have been developed is shown in upper left hand picture.

Fernspray Retinospora
This is a variety of very finely cut foliage, and frond-like branches. Botanically known as Chamaecyparis obtusa filicoides.

Dwarf Hinoki Cypress
This is an extremely dwarf tree of slow growth, having small crinkled foliage resembling small rosettes.

Chamaecyparis Lutescens
A form of yellowish color.

Moss Retinospora

Sawara Cypress (Chamaecyparis pisifera)

Like the other forms of Chamaecyparis described, this tree has also provided a large number of horticultural varieties. These are mostly similar, except for slight variations of foliage, form, or color.

A number of the most interesting horticultural varieties of the Sawara Cypress are illustrated.

Sawara Cypress
This is the species from which other trees of this group originated.

Plume Retinospora
This variety is noticeably more hardy than many of the others.

There is an aspect of grace and dignity about Hemlocks which, together with their ability to add a touch of green to a shady spot, makes them of great value in ornamental use. The several trees in the background are Hemlock. The low plant near the wall is a Dwarf Japanese Yew. Refer to Hemlock chapter page 286.

Chapter XLIV

Cypress (Cupressus)

T HE Cypress family, since it has been separated from the Chamaecyparis, is composed of about twelve species, growing in a wild state along the Pacific Coast in North America, extending into Mexico, in the southwestern states, and in a wide area in the southern part of Europe, extending to China.

All of the Cypress are of a more or less tender nature, and none of this family are planted successfully in the territory adjacent to Chicago. They do, however, form an important and popular group which is widely used in less severe climates.

References in literature to the Cypress are very numerous. It is one of the oldest of cultivated Evergreens, as it is found in its native stands in those parts of the world which are much older in civilization than our own country.

Young specimen of Italian Cypress

Very old planting of Italian Cypress showing the characteristic spire-like development which has made these trees such great favorites throughout the countries of southern Europe, as well as in California and other warm climates.

Arizona Cypress

Funeral Cypress, or Mourning Cypress, is another species with which most everyone is familiar by name, although this tree is not an important ornamental variety. A list of the various species and varieties of Cypress, together with a detailed picture of the foliage of this tree, is shown on page 48.

CRYPTOMERIA

This family consists of but one species, which has a number of horticultural varieties. It is a tree native to Japan. It is not of sufficient hardiness to plant in the central west, but is used extensively in warmer climates, as well as in some localities in the east. The picture shown is one of the best-known horticultural varieties, Lobb's Cryptomeria.

Lobb's Cryptomeria

The Cypress most widely-known, no doubt, is the Italian Cypress. Visitors to California are always impressed with the Monterey Cypress, a picturesque tree which grows in a limited area in California. Another quite well-known tree is the Arizona Cypress, a species somewhat more hardy, and well-suited to the hot, dry conditions of the southwest, where it is extensively planted in Texas, Arizona, and in that locality. The

Chapter XLV

Junipers (Juniperus)

THERE is no family of Evergreens, hardy in the north, that includes so large a number of trees of different habits of growth as we find in the Junipers. Unlike many of the other genera of Evergreens, composed of species all quite similar in general character, the Junipers have a wide range of shapes, from very narrow, spire-like specimens, to those which creep along the ground.

This family is the most important one in ornamental landscape work in the vicinity of northern Illinois and localities of similar climate. The various forms, as pictured in the following pages, cover the leading species and horticultural varieties. While there are approximately thirty species of Junipers, the majority of all species commonly found in landscape plantings are composed of the following species or their varieties: *Juniperus Virginiana* (Redcedar), the common Juniper of North America; *Juniperus chinensis* (Chinese Juniper), native of China and Asiatic countries; *Juniperus communis* (Common Juniper), native in North America and throughout Europe, which has a great many horticultural forms; *Juniperus sabina* (Savin Juniper), from southern Europe, which also has many horticultural forms, and *Juniperus scopulorum* (Colorado Juniper), another native American species having some very interesting and beautiful variations, which are shown in these pages.

Foliage of Juniper

The Junipers have a unique advantage over many other genera of Evergreens from the fact that they thrive in almost all parts of the country. They are able to withstand the severe cold of the north, and also the opposite conditions in the extreme south. The growth of course, is much faster in the south, but they are very satisfactory over almost the entire United States. As a general rule, Junipers do better in an open, sunny location and a light soil. All are easily trimmed and may thus be kept small for many years.

JUNIPERS

CHINESE JUNIPER (Juniperus chinensis)

This is a native Juniper of Asia, where it covers large areas. Needles are sharp and prickly. Color of needles is light green, with a slightly bluish cast. Average size at maturity fifteen to twenty feet.

As shown in the three pictures

Chinese Juniper. This is the mother plant from which a number of horticultural varieties, as illustrated in the following pages, are grown. For a complete list of the horticultural varieties of this tree see page 48.

on this page, there is a wide variance in the habit of growth of this tree. Some trees are broad and bushy, and they vary to those of extremely narrow form.

COLUMN CHINESE JUNIPER (Juniperus chinensis pyramidalis)

This variety is one introduced probably thirty years ago by the United States Department of Agriculture, Bureau of Plant Industry. It was discovered in China by Frank Meyer, plant explorer. As shown in this picture, which is a photograph of one of the original trees in Washington, D. C., superimposed on a suitable background, this tree is of extremely columnar habit. In order to produce trees of this narrow form, some attention to trimming is necessary.

Column Chinese Juniper

There are two distinct trees which are grown and sold under this name. One is the blue form as pictured; the other is similar, except that it is green in color.

Like others of this Chinese Juniper family, it requires open, sunny location and prefers a light soil, well drained. It grows very rapidly, particularly in the warmer sections of this country. It gives planters in the colder localities a tree which closely resembles the Italian Cypress in habit of growth. The needles are sharp and prickly. It generally grows with one stem, in contrast to some of the *Juniperus communis* types of Juniper which have numerous vertical stems.

WHITE LEAF CHINESE JUNIPER

(Juniperus chinensis albovariegata)

The peculiar characteristic of this horticultural variety of the Chinese Juniper is the white, variegated tips which appear throughout the tree. It is a close, compact, upright grower, an interesting addition to the group of solid green trees.

There are, among the Chinese Juniper, some forms which are golden-tipped, some are drooping in habit, some which have a prominence of the juvenile or whipcord foliage, and some which are composed entirely of the prickly, sharp needles. Nurserymen have been able to fix these characteristics by skillful selection and propagation.

White Leaf Chinese Juniper

By staking Pfitzer Juniper, when small, they may be made to grow in an upright habit as shown in this picture. See next page for description of the Pfitzer Juniper.

PFITZER JUNIPER
(Juniperus chinensis pfitzeriana)

This is the most widely-planted and generally satisfactory of all the Junipers. It has a very robust and thrifty constitution. Unlike most of the other Junipers, it will stand considerable shade, but it does well in full, open sun also.

It originated thirty-five or forty years ago in Pfitzer's Nursery near Berlin, Germany, and immediately became popular throughout Europe and America. It makes a rapid growth, but may be easily trimmed. It is not uncommon to find specimens as much as twenty feet in diameter. The foliage is green with a slight tinge of blue, some strains being quite decidedly bluish in color. It is extensively used in foundation plantings, as it makes a low, bushy growth, ideal for uses of this kind.

SARGENT JUNIPER (Juniperus chinensis sargenti)

This interesting tree was introduced to the Arnold Arboretum by Prof. Sargent, who collected seeds in Japan in 1892. Ernest Wilson, in his book, "The Conifers and Taxads of Japan," writes: "It has proved perfectly hardy, grows freely, and its stems and branchlets overlap one another in such a manner as to form neat, low, wide-spreading masses of green. As a ground cover, this Juniper is the most valuable of all the known kinds." The planting which is shown in this picture bordering a walk is, or course, composed of many plants growing together.

A single specimen of Sargent Juniper.

It is not more than eight to twelve inches in height and creeps along the ground to considerable distance. For this reason it is an ideal tree for terraces, for ground cover, or for a border to taller trees. It also serves a good purpose in rock gardens.

While not all Nurseries separate this tree into two distinct forms, there is a type with green foliage and slightly different foliage texture, and another type with bluish foliage of the shade shown in this colored print. While this tree is said to grow wild in Japan, it is regarded as a horticultural variety of Chinese Juniper, or, more properly speaking, a variation of this tree the habit of which doubtless is a result of environment.

Several Sargent Junipers planted together to form a low border.

Prostrate Juniper (Juniperus communis depressa)

The Prostrate Juniper in a foundation planting.

Prostrate Juniper
(Juniperus communis depressa)

This is a native American Juniper, growing over an extended area in the North Central states, particularly in Minnesota, Wisconsin, Michigan, and New England. The typical growth is low and spreading, as shown on the hillside planting on the opposite page.

The extremities of the branches are usually ascending but rarely to a greater height than three feet. The leaves are sharply pointed, rather grayish green, marked on the upper surface by broad, white bands. The underside of the needles is silvery green. It is a most vigorous grower, having many stems, thriving to best advantage on gravelly or sandy hillsides fully exposed to the sun.

There is also a golden form, as shown in the colored picture, which is thought to have originated many years ago in the old Douglas Nurseries at Waukegan, Illinois.

Vase Shaped Prostrate Juniper
(Juniperus communis depressa)

This horticultural variety is one introduced by the D. Hill Nursery Company. It is an improvement over the typical form, both in the habit of growth, which is more erect and regular as shown in this picture, and in the hardiness of the tree. There is a tendency in the seedling variety to develop dead wood and dead branches here and there from time to time. This tendency has been largely overcome in this new vase-shaped form.

Vase Shaped Prostrate Juniper.

Irish Juniper

IRISH JUNIPER
(Juniperus communis hibernica)

This tree is considered a horticultural variety of the *Juniperus communis,* the common Juniper of Europe, although it grows wild in some localities in Ireland and elsewhere. It is one of the oldest of the ornamental Evergreens, having been widely used for years. It is, however, slightly tender and, except in localities having mild winters, it is frequently burned on the tips. It also has the disadvantage of being rather easily damaged by snow. It forms numerous stems which grow vertically from the base of the tree. These stems have to be tied together to keep it in good condition.

It has a striking appearance and makes a fine specimen, where trees of small growth and formal lines are wanted. The foliage is prickly, whitish beneath. It cannot be successfully planted much farther north than northern Illinois. If untrimmed, it will reach twenty feet in height. Diameter at the base is about eighteen inches.

SWEDISH JUNIPER
(Juniperus communis suecica)

This is a Juniper from the north of Europe, more hardy than the Irish Juniper, but quite similar in appearance. The foliage is light, yellowish-green in color. It generally grows to a height of ten or twelve feet, and sometimes, taller.

Swedish Juniper

The berries of the Juniper are used for medicinal purposes and in the manufacturing of spirits. Evidence of this latter fact is contained in these lines of Tennyson:

"*The Birch Tree swang her fragrant hair;*
The Bramble cast her berry;
The gin within the Juniper
Began to make him merry."

Andorra Juniper

(Juniperus communis depressa plumosa)

This is a comparatively new variety. It was found in 1907 in a shipment of wild seedlings of the Prostrate Juniper (*Juniperus communis depressa*) collected in Maine and sent to the Andorra Nurseries. The tree, however, bears very little, if any, resemblance to the species *Juniperus communis*. It has more of the characteristics of the Savin Juniper (*Juniperus sabina*). However, it is generally regarded as a horticultural variety of the *Juniperus communis*.

Its habit of growth, as shown in the colored picture below, is low and spreading. Plants seldom reach more than fifteen inches in height, but spread out to a considerable area.

Its main distinction is the unusual, pinkish coloring of the foliage when frost comes in the fall. The colored picture shows the tree as it appears in the early fall months after the first severe frost. It retains this color until spring, when it changes to a grayish-green color.

Listed in *The Cultivated Conifers,* by Bailey, as *Juniperus horizontalis var. plumosa.*

The low trees in front are the Andorra Juniper. Those in the immediate background are the Silver Redcedar (Juniperus virginiana glauca), which have been quite severely trimmed. This photograph was taken on the grounds of the Hill Nursery Company, Dundee, Illinois.

SPINY GREEK JUNIPER
(Juniperus excelsa stricta)

This tree is a horticultural variety of the *Juniperus excelsa,* a tree which covers an extensive region in southern Europe, and which is of variable dimensions in different localities. The variety Stricta shown in this picture is the best known horticultural variety. It has a tapering outline, very dense in growth, and a glaucous foliage, giving the plant a grayish white appearance. While it is considered hardy in the region of northern Illinois, it does much better in the eastern states.

WAUKEGAN JUNIPER
(Juniperus horizontalis douglasi)

This tree takes its name from the locality around Waukegan, Illinois, where this type of Juniper grows along the bluffs of Lake Michigan. It is a selected type, having soft, whipcord foliage, and an attractive, pinkish, winter color, as shown in the picture below. It was introduced many years ago by the Hill Nursery Co.

Spiny Greek Juniper

Waukegan Juniper

This specimen was photographed on the grounds of the Hill Nursery Company.

JAPANESE JUNIPER (Juniperus japonica)

The famous Arnold Arboretum in one of their bulletins says of this tree, "This is the best known of the Prostrate Junipers which Japan has sent to the gardens of America. It is a plant with wide-spreading, creeping stems, bluish green. It has sharply pointed leaves, marked on the upper surface by two white lines. It is perfectly hardy." Very old plants will reach a considerable diameter. It is not uncommon to find specimens six to eight feet across, with a height of only eight to twelve inches. It may, however, be maintained at a smaller size by trimming the branches.

Some planters may be familiar with this tree under the name *Juniperus chinensis procumbens,* a name which designated this tree until the more recent name given above was adopted.

Bar Harbor Juniper (Juniperus sabina horizontalis)

Bar Harbor Juniper (Juniperus sabina horizontalis)

Growing wild in many localities in the United States is a species of Juniper loosely described as *Juniperus horizontalis*. Its characteristics vary in different localities. Its identification is, therefore, very difficult. Many of these plants have been taken by nurserymen and propagated. The form pictured above, which has its native home on the Coast of Maine, remains one of the most attractive and widely used forms. The color is a beautiful soft blue, which makes it unusually attractive.

Hill Japanese Juniper

This is a most interesting variation of the Japanese Juniper described on the opposite page. An extremely dwarf and slow growing form. This is an ideal tree for use where trees of dwarf nature are desired. The tree in this picture is only eighteen inches in spread, but is twelve years old.

Hill Japanese Juniper

Savin Juniper (Juniperus sabina)

This is a low, many-branched shrub, sometimes growing four feet in height. It is native in the lower Alps in southern Europe. It also occurs in the Pyrenees, in Spain, and in Greece, but always as a mountain plant. Its

The tree in inset shows the character and branching habit of the Savin Juniper. Two specimens are shown in the foreground of planting. Other trees in the planting are Redcedar and Colorado Blue Spruce.

branches are spreading, dense, clothed with short, straight, tufted branchlets. It has blackish-purple or dark violet berries about the size of small currants. This is one of the oldest of ornamental Evergreens, as it was mentioned in Turner's "Names of Herbs," which was published almost four hundred years ago. The Savin Juniper has certain medicinal properties which have long been known. In consequence of this, its planting in former times was prohibited in France.

Tamarix Savin Juniper (Juniperus sabina tamariscifolia)

It is more of a low, spreading shrub than the true Savin Juniper, and has very fine needles named from the resemblance which the needles bear to the leaves of the Tamarix. It has been replaced in recent years in ornamental plantings by some of the other trees of similar habit, particularly the Sargent Juniper and the Japanese Juniper. While it is of a hardy nature, it has an unfortunate tendency to develop dead branches and dead wood from time to time, so that it is less used now than formerly. It still remains, however, one of the oldest and best known of the low growing Junipers. It has an attractive bluish-green coloring.

This plant likewise has been in cultivation for hundreds of years.

Tamarix Savin Juniper

Von Ehron Juniper

(Juniperus sabina von ehron)

This horticultural variety of the Savin Juniper is not so well known. It is seldom seen in plantings. It is a very fast grower. This gives it a more loose and open appearance, quite different from the Savin Juniper. Judging from the name of this tree, it doubtless originated in one of the nurseries of Holland. It has a deep rich color, and bears both juvenile and adult foliage.

Von Ehron Juniper

Hill Silver Juniper

Colorado or Rocky Mountain Juniper (Juniperus scopulorum)

This is an American tree which extends over a wide range, from north to south, from South Dakota and Montana down through Colorado, as well as in certain areas on the Pacific Coast.

When grown from seed, it is one of the most variable of Junipers, and produces trees which run from those of extremely narrow habit, to wide, spreading specimens. There is also a great difference in the color and foliage characteristics among the varieties grown from seed.

This species was the hobby of the late D. Hill. He experimented with this tree for more than thirty years, personally selecting unusual types in the Black Hills of South Dakota, from which he developed a large number of distinct varieties, some of which are briefly described below.

Hill Silver Juniper is the one which has gained greatest popularity among the forms of the *Juniperus scopulorum*. As shown in the colored picture on the opposite page, it is of unusual, bluish color and of an attractive, compact growth. Unlike many varieties of Evergreens, this tree is brightest in color during the summer months. Dry weather brings out the color to best advantage. It is not a large-growing tree, probably never reaching more than twenty feet, but it can be trimmed and maintained at a smaller size.

Moonlight Juniper has none of the typical, needle-like formation of foliage of Junipers, but runs to the whipcord foliage, of very light blue color. This peculiar characteristic gives it an unusual appearance.

Blue Moon Juniper is a silvery blue type, which has fine delicate foliage. It grows in a broad, pyramidal shape.

North Star Juniper—In contrast to the blue coloring of almost all the other types of *Juniperus scopulorum,* this tree has fine whipcord foliage of a light, shiny, green color. It grows in a shapely conical form of compact habit.

Silver Queen Juniper differs from the others in its very narrow growth and closely growing branches, which ascend almost vertically. It does not spread more than eighteen to twenty inches.

Hill Weeping Juniper was found in northern Montana, which assures us of its extreme hardiness. It has long and graceful drooping branchlets, which give the tree an almost tropical appearance. There is another form grown by the Hill Nursery Company called Weeping Colorado Juniper, it has an even more weeping tendency, as the branchlets are somewhat longer and finer foliaged.

Other Varieties—In addition to those sorts mentioned above, there are numerous other forms which have been named and propagated, having slightly differing characteristics. There is at least one golden type not yet generally available, as well as a number of selected silvery foliaged varieties.

RED CEDAR (Juniperus Virginiana)

REDCEDAR (Juniperus Virginiana)

This tree, misnamed "cedar," is one of America's best-known Evergreens. Nature planted it over almost all the North American continent, from Canada to Florida. It is, very likely, found in every state east of the Rocky Mountains. It is frequently seen along country roads, pastures, and hillsides, as well as in dry and rocky places. It is, therefore, quite natural that the different conditions under which it grows in a native state have produced a very extensive variation in the characteristics of this tree. There are tall and narrow types, low and bushy shapes, and all intermediate shapes found in various locations. One type is quite extensively referred to as the Eastern type; another the Platte River type, which grows in the vicinity of the Platte River in Nebraska; the Wisconsin and Minnesota types, which are frequently very narrow, compact and unusually attractive; and the Tennessee type.

This tree was one of the first which was cultivated for an ornament, and during the many years which it has been planted, there have been almost no end of horticultural varieties selected, named, and introduced throughout the world. In this book, on page 50, are a number of the best known of these horticultural varieties, and throughout the following pages, many of these types are illustrated and described. Redcedar, because of its wide native distribution, is well suited to planting almost anywhere throughout the United States. It grows naturally oftentimes on gravelly hillsides, and it is, therefore, excellent for planting in poor, sandy soil. It does best where it has plenty of circulation of air and full sunlight.

The wood of the Redcedar is an important commercial product, especially noted for its ability to resist moisture. Also, because of the peculiar fragrance of this wood, it is frequently used in cedar chests and in similar ways to resist moths. The heart wood is of a handsome, dark red color, which takes a fine polish. Like other Junipers, it produces bright blue and silver berries, which are a great attraction to birds.

As winter approaches, the tips of the new foliage become pinkish or reddish in color. The early spring color is very bright green, gradually darkening throughout the Summer. It may very readily be trimmed and shaped into various forms. In fact, it requires trimming, especially when small, to develop an attractive and compact habit of growth. They vary in size in their ultimate growth, from twenty to even one hundred feet.

A well developed Redcedar about twelve feet tall.

Cannart Redcedar

Cannart Redcedar (Juniperus virginiana cannarti)
(Picture on opposite page)

This horticultural variety of the Red Cedar has long been one of the leading favorites. It has a deep, rich, green color and runs largely to the whipcord foliage rather than the needle formation. It is a tree which probably would reach, under normal conditions, up to twenty feet, but may be kept trimmed to smaller proportions. It also has unusually bluish and powdery berries, which frequently occur in large clusters and give the tree a most unusual feature.

Another tree which quite closely resembles the Cannart Redcedar is the Schott Redcedar. It is distinguished by a somewhat lighter green color and a more ascending habit of the branchlet tips. In some nurseries these two trees are mixed, but there is a quite noticeable difference when they are seen side by side.

Hill Pyramidal Juniper (Juniperus virginiana pyramidalis hilli)

This is an attractive, compact grower, which has rich, dark green foliage. The whipcord foliage predominates. It is a very rapid grower, capable of being trimmed into numerous forms. The natural tendency of this tree is to grow with many stems from the ground, forming an erect bush, but, by training when small, upright specimens are easily produced. This tree is frequently trimmed into ball shapes for formal uses.

Goldtip Redcedar (Juniper virginiana elegantissima)

This tree has been for many years known under the name of Lee's Golden Juniper, one of the brightest and most colorful of the Junipers. It might be described as a bronze green, overlaid with pale yellow. Its value lies largely in the contrasting appearance which this tree makes when planted in groups with those of darker color. It is the natural tendency of this tree to grow rather low and spreading. Most nurseries, however, stake it when small, so as to develop a growth similar to that shown in the picture. It shows its best color when planted in an open location in rich soil. In the spring, when the new growth comes out, the color is most pronounced.

Goldtip Redcedar

Silver Redcedar

SILVER REDCEDAR (Juniperus virginiana glauca)

This is among the outstanding of the horticultural varieties of the Redcedar. It has been known for a great many years, as it appears in old nursery catalogs of English concerns more than sixty years old. Its most outstanding feature is the silvery blue color, which is brightest in spring, darkening somewhat as the season progresses. The new growth is of almost a whitish-blue color.

It is one of the few Evergreens which thrive over the entire country, making a satisfactory tree in the south as well as in the northern states. It grows quite rapidly, eventually reaching twenty feet or more, but may be easily trimmed and maintained in a smaller size. It must be trimmed at least once a year in order to produce the compactness of growth as shown in the picture on opposite page. By more frequent trimming, it may be grown into specimens of extreme, formal outline.

Like other Junipers of similar characteristics, this tree is of great value in landscaping, not only because of its color, but because it is readily adapted to smaller areas such as foundation-plantings. It makes a beautiful hedge and stands severe trimming very well.

KOSTER REDCEDAR
(Juniperus virginiana kosteri)

This is a low and spreading tree with bluish-green leaves. It has a tendency to produce rather long, stiff branches, giving it an in-between habit of growth, being somewhat less tall in growth than Pfitzer Juniper, and higher than the creeping forms.

It is not so well known, although it is an old variety. It grows quite rapidly and reaches a considerable size in a few years. There is some question as to whether it is a true *Virginiana* variety, as it shows characteristics resembling the *Juniperus sabina* family.

Koster Redcedar

HILL DUNDEE JUNIPER

(Juniperus virginiana pyramidiformia hilli)

This tree is considered one of the most valuable of Junipers introduced within recent years. It originated from a specimen found in the Hill Nursery about twenty-five years ago. The picture above, unfortunately, is not a true representation of the beauty of this tree. It is a specimen which has been rather too severely trimmed. The color of the Dundee Juniper is bluish-green in the spring and summer, and purplish-plum color in the fall and winter. This is not the bronze color of the Redcedar, but an unusual shade different from any other Evergreens. It is propagated by grafting, as are all forms of the *Juniperus virginiana* mentioned in the preceding pages.

MEYER JUNIPER
(Juniperus squamata
meyeri)

This is one of the newer Evergreens, one which was found in China and introduced by the late Frank N. Meyer. It makes a peculiar, bunchy growth and is distinct in its unusual coloring. The leaves are plump, pointed, and prickly, and of a bright, shiny, blue color. The foliage appears of different colors when viewed from different angles. There are tones of green, white and pinkish red. The growth is irregular.

European Larch

Umbrella Pine

EUROPEAN LARCH
(Larix europea)

Although there are a number of species of the Larch, it is not an important ornamental Evergreen. It is, however, one of the oldest cultivated trees. The European Larch, which is pictured here, is the one best-suited for ornamental uses. The American Larch, or Tamarack, is a swamp tree, less desirable for ornamental uses. The Larch is a deciduous conifer. Unlike the great majority of other Evergreens, it sheds its needles in the fall. Its chief attraction lies in the delicate beauty of the new spring growth, and in the beautiful, yellowish color of the needles just before they shed in the fall. It makes a tree of immense size. It is a quite rapid grower. The genera is native throughout the colder sections of Europe, Asia and America. It grows in an upright pyramidal habit with regular conical form. Leaves are light green.

UMBRELLA PINE
(Sciadopitys verticillata)

This interesting and unusual genera is composed of a single species, and, while it is not an important ornamental plant, it is an interesting and unusual tree. It is a native of central Japan. It is one of the more tender trees, growing in northern Illinois only in sheltered positions. Its name is derived from the peculiar clusters of the needles, which somewhat resemble a miniature umbrella.

CHAPTER XLVI

Spruce (Picea)

SPRUCES comprise one of the most important genera of Evergreens for planters in the northern part of the United States. They are primarily cold-loving trees and do not thrive in the South or other localities where the temperature is too warm. They are at their best in southern Minnesota, central Wisconsin, and similar latitudes. They do, however, prove satisfactory much farther south, as many plantings of Spruce are seen in Oklahoma and other of the bordering southern states.

In this book, on pages 51 and 52, are more than thirty species of the Spruce with a large number of horticultural varieties. Many of the most important species and varieties are described in the following pages.

Spruces are natives of the United States, particularly in the Rocky Mountain area, the Great Lakes States, and in the northwestern Pacific Coast area extending into Alaska. They are also extensively found throughout Canada. The Spruces likely hold the farthermost northern outpost of tree life. They are known to grow within the Arctic Circle. Japan, as well as some of the other Asiatic countries, has furnished us with some species of Spruce; quite a large group of these which are not yet generally available in nurseries, have been introduced within recent years from Asia.

Spruces have been widely planted for many hundreds of years. This fact, no doubt, accounts for the many horticultural varieties which exist. A description of the foliage characteristics of Spruces as compared to other genera of Evergreens will be found in chapter 7.

BLACK HILLS SPRUCE (Picea canadensis albertiana)

Black Hills Spruce is considered a close relative of White Spruce, having developed its distinct characteristics through centuries of living in the Black Hills country of South Dakota. The foliage varies from green to a bluish tint; some are as blue as a Colorado Blue Spruce, and all trees are remarkable for their bright, fresh color.

This is one of the hardiest of all Spruces. It grows unusually symmetrical, compact and bushy. This characteristic is evident in even the very smallest trees, which develop into round, sturdy, compact trees even when small. As the tree grows and develops, it continues to carry this particular style of growth. It reaches twenty-five to forty feet, with a ten to twelve-foot spread of branches. Being a slow grower, it can remain in close quarters for several years.

Oriental Spruce   *Engelmann Spruce*

ENGELMANN SPRUCE (Picea engelmanni)

This is an American species extending from New Mexico over a large area to the north, at altitudes of eight thousand to twelve thousand feet. It is named for Dr. Engelmann, who first recognized it as a separate species and introduced it to cultivation about 1860. It makes a narrow, pyramidal tree, most frequently of dark green foliage, but, as with the Colorado Blue Spruce, occasionally exceptionally blue trees develop. For this reason it is difficult for the uninformed to distinguish it from the Colorado Blue Spruce. However, the Engelmann Spruce is noted for the particularly strong odor of its crushed needles. It also has a pubescent or hairy growth on its twigs and branchlets, in contrast to the Colorado Blue Spruce which is non-pubescent. The branches are stiff and the needles sharply pointed. In its native state it reaches up to one hundred fifty feet, but in cultivation is seldom found more than thirty to forty feet in height. Doubtless because of the fact that its native home is in high altitudes, it thrives to best advantage in cooler localities.

ORIENTAL SPRUCE (Picea orientalis)

This native of Asia Minor and the Caucasus Mountains bears close resemblance to the familiar Norway Spruce. However, it has exceedingly fine, short leaves, and in this respect the needles are the shortest of all Spruces, averaging one-fourth inch in length. It makes a rapid pyramidal growth and has attractive compact form. Needles are dark green, blunt on the ends and glossy. It is a tree frequently seen in the eastern sections, but seldom planted in the Middle West. It is recommended for planting on poor, gravelly soil where it thrives contrary to the usual behavior of Spruces.

Norway Spruce

Norway Spruce (Picea excelsa)

This tree is doubtless more familiar, at least to persons in the northern and eastern states, than any other Evergreen. It has been planted for so many years, and so extensively, that it is looked upon almost as a native species. Its tall, drooping, dark, somber, green color is a familiar sight along country roads, in old cemeteries, and around farm homes. This tree, together with the European Larch and the Scotch Pine, comprised the first plantings made in the Hill Nursery Company in 1855.

Norway Spruce is widely distributed throughout central Europe, obtaining great size and girth, up to two hundred feet. Because of its wide distribution, there is some variance in the characteristics of the trees from different localities. Generally, those seeds collected from the more northern latitudes are superior.

Having been grown for ornamental uses for several hundred years, it is only to be expected that a large number of horticultural varieties has developed. There is no complete, definite list of such varieties. Anyone interested will find on page 51 the names of about fifty of these varieties, although this list is by no means complete. In the following pages some of the most interesting of these forms, many of them dwarf forms, are described.

As valuable and well liked as this tree is, throughout the United States, it has no doubt been responsible to a large extent for a certain prejudice against Evergreens, for the reason that it has long been associated in our minds with the older cemeteries.

It is thoroughly hardy, robust, and thrifty both on damp and on higher dry soil, and will doubtless remain, for generations to come, one of the most familiar sights of the American landscape, particularly in the central western states.

Nest Shaped Spruce (Picea excelsa nidiformis)

This dwarf form was found in cultivation near Hamburg, Germany. It was described by the introducer many years ago as "a round, plate-like, fan-forming form, with a dense, nest-like mass of branchlets where the leading shoot should be." It is of such extraordinary dense growth, so densely branched, that one wonders how the light ever gets to the inner branches. Its branchlets are in tight layers, the whole forming a dense, impenetrable head.

It grows very slowly—three-fourths to one and three-fourths inches yearly.

Nest Shaped Spruce

White Spruce

White Spruce (Picea canadensis)

This tree might well be considered our most common native Spruce. Its natural range extends to within the Arctic Circle, as it is found growing along the Coppermine River. It extends through Canada from Alaska to the east coast and forms an extensive belt from Montana throughout northern Wisconsin, Minnesota, Michigan, and into New York State. The foliage is bluish-green, some specimens having a very bluish color. It is a compact, regular-growing tree of conical outline, most attractive when small. In old age it is not as permanently satisfactory as the Norway Spruce, and it gains much less height, seldom growing more than twenty-five to fifty feet. While it resembles the Black Spruce and the Red Spruce to some extent, it thrives to a better advantage under hot, dry conditions than either of the above mentioned sorts.

In addition to its value as an ornamental tree, it is one of the most important sources of pulp for paper making.

In addition to its uses for screens, backgrounds, windbreaks and other places where tall bushy specimens are required, it is extensively planted for hedges. It makes a very satisfactory tree for this purpose.

Maxwell Spruce (Picea excelsa maxwelli)

This dwarf Spruce is one of the best known and oldest forms. It was raised about fifty years ago in the Maxwell Nursery, Geneva, New York.

Its growth is very slow, averaging less than one inch per year. Needles are extremely fine, running from one-fourth to one-half inch in length. Many other less desirable forms are often sold as Maxwell Spruce, thus capitalizing on the name of this well known dwarf tree. Another dwarf form is the Pygmy Spruce (*Picea excelsa pygmaea*).

Maxwell Spruce

Pygmy Spruce

Dwarf Alberta Spruce (Picea glauca conica)

This is one of the most interesting oddities among Evergreens. It is of extremely close, pyramidal growth, thickly covered with short, close-set, twiggy branches and clothed in grass-green leaves. It is unlike any other Evergreen, both in shape and general appearance, so that it always attracts attention.

The parent tree is in the Arnold Arboretum, at Jamaica Plain, Massachusetts. It was found in the Canadian Rockies at Lake Laggan in 1904, by Mr. J. G. Jack, of the Arnold Arboretum staff. Its annual growth is only one-half inch to one inch, so that many years are required to raise the trees in the nursery.

Dwarf Alberta Spruce

Some of the oldest trees in the country are said to be about five feet high, still retaining their characteristic habits.

It is perfectly hardy in this climate, but there is only one danger for which we must look out. If exposed to the south, this little tree may be burned by the winter sun and winds. Snow, which easily collects in the dense branches, will, if melted by the sun, change to ice and have the effect of a lens. No serious damage will then result except a browning and shedding of some of the needles. It is advisable, therefore, to shade it toward the south during winter. This is easily done by fastening a piece of burlap to two stakes, and setting this protection at the south side of the trees.

It prefers a partially shaded, rather moist location, and winter protection is then unnecessary.

Many planting uses suggest themselves for this little tree. For formal effect in terraces and gardens and rock gardens, it is proving of great interest and value.

TIGERTAIL SPRUCE (Picea polita)

As the illustration indicates, this Spruce possesses a unique character which makes its identification easy. The needles are extremely stiff and sharply pointed, as one writer describes it, "like the point of a perch's fin." The foliage of old trees bears close resemblance to a tiger's tail, which gives the tree its peculiar name.

It is found in pure forests in restricted localities in Japan. The late E. H. Wilson has described a forest of a pure stand of this tree as one of the finest and most unique sylvicultural sights he ever saw. It is not among the hardiest of the Spruces, but certainly deserves a place as one of the most distinct and interesting of this family. It was introduced into the United States about 1862. It has orange-red branchlets, which give it an added contrast of appearance.

OTHER SPRUCES

Unfortunately space does not allow a description of more of the Spruces. Some which might be briefly mentioned as worthy of a place are

Tigertail Spruce

Alcock Spruce (*Picea alcockiana*), Black Spruce (*Picea mariana*), and Sitka Spruce (*Picea sitchensis*). Alcock Spruce, a Japanese species, is one introduced to cultivation through the visit of John Gould Veitch to Japan in 1860. Its most noticeable characteristic is the contrast between the deep green of the lower side of the leaves and the light silvery color of the upper side.

The Black Spruce is the well known swamp Spruce found extensively throughout Wisconsin, Minnesota and elsewhere. It is not highly regarded as an ornamental tree, but is very useful under certain conditions of planting.

The Sitka Spruce forms a most important timber tree in Washington and Oregon, extending into Alaska in a narrow belt extending inland not more than forty or fifty miles. It is the largest of all the Spruces. It is seldom seen in ornamental landscape plantings.

Weeping Norway Spruce

Weeping Norway Spruce (Picea excelsa pendula)

Among the Spruces, as well as in other genera of Evergreens, are occasionally found oddities in the form of so called weeping growth as illustrated in the picture on page 245. This particular tree is on the grounds of Mrs. T. B. Cook, Cooksburg, Pennsylvania, who purchased the tree from the Hill Nursery about thirty years ago.

There is a weeping variety of the Colorado Blue Spruce which appears quite similar, except of course for the texture and color of the foliage.

While trees of this character have very little practical value, they are interesting examples of the freaks and oddities which nature sometimes produces.

The Blue Spruces

Few Evergreens have obtained the popularity of the Blue Spruces. The seedling form known as the Colorado Blue Spruce (*Picea pungens glauca*) is native to an extensive region in the Rocky Mountains, extending from New Mexico north, most extensively in Colorado. It is a magnificent tree in its native stands. Those of the most bluish color are found in deep gorges of high altitudes.

When planted from seed, a small proportion of the trees develops the bright blue color. The great majority are of greenish cast, or only a slightly bluish tendency. The form which is most generally planted and for which greatest demand exists, is the selected trees with the bright blue foliage. Like many of the highly-colored Evergreens, this bluish color is a bloom or sheen, a sort of powdery substance on the outside of the needles. For this reason its color is less pronounced during the winter months, and brightest during the late spring and summer.

While the seedling form makes a beautiful and symmetrical tree, it is but seldom that an unusual blue specimen develops. For this reason, many of the more choice trees to be seen in plantings are one of a number of selected horticultural varieties which have been propagated by grafting.

Chief among these is the Koster Blue Spruce, a variety of many years standing, originally selected and propagated by one of the leading nurseries of Holland, which name it bears. Grafted trees are uniform in color, all reproducing bright blue color.

Another Blue Spruce of more recent introduction is called the Moerheim Spruce. This is said to possess an even more pronounced color than the Koster Spruce. There are also some less known blue forms, as well as a golden variety and a weeping variety. The growth of the Blue Spruce is generally very symmetrical in the seedling type. Grafted trees are apt to be irregular in growth until they have reached a height of five or six feet or more; then they carry a type of growth in symmetrical whorls.

Koster Blue Spruce

Servian Spruce

SERVIAN SPRUCE
(Picea omorica)

This tree has a very restricted distribution along the river Drina on the boundary of Serbia. The growth is very slender; the branch spread, narrow and symmetrical. The leaves are from one-half to three-fourths inch in length. The true form has been scarce in cultivation because of the great difficulties of securing seed.

It has been with some difficulty that we have been able to show a picture of a good specimen of this tree. After trying to locate such a picture in this country, the photograph was secured from a nurseryman friend in Vienna. It well illustrates the striking and most unusual character of this tree. The Servian Spruce is one of a limited group of Spruces which closely resembles Firs in appearance because of flat needles, unlike the usual four-sided needles of the Spruces. However, it is included in the family of Spruces for other botanical reasons.

It is a fact of considerable scientific interest that this tree bears close affinity with the Sitka Spruce of northwest Pacific Coast fame, and at the same time it has no near relatives in its own vicinity, being entirely different from the Oriental Spruce and the Norway Spruce, both of which grow in the same region.

CHAPTER XLVII

Pines (Pinus)

TO many people, "Pine" is synonymous with Evergreen; it is a term which designates in their minds the entire Evergreen family. Specifically, however, it applies to an extensive family of more than seventy-five species which extend throughout the world, mostly in the northern hemisphere, but also in higher altitudes in the semi-tropics. As a source of timber, Pines rank first in the United States. Commercially, they might be divided into groups: the hard Pines, the soft Pines, the Pines which produce turpentine and rosin, and the Pines which produce edible seeds or nuts.

Botanically, they are divided into groups according to certain similar characteristics which exist between many related species. From an ornamental standpoint, however, no such easy division may be made. Pines are one of the most readily recognized genera of Evergreens. The needles are always arranged in bundles, and, with but few exceptions, the needles are in two's, three's, or five's, with a papery sheath at their base. This peculiar trait is a sure insignia, as no other Evergreens have this characteristic.

With the exception of a few dwarf species, Pines are among the taller, massive trees. Some Pines rank among the largest of the Evergreens which grow in North America. On the Pacific slope there are many valuable and most interesting Pines, few of which are capable of withstanding conditions elsewhere within the United States.

In this book on pages 52 to 54 are listed approximately fifty of the best-known species, together with a number of the most important horticultural varieties. In the following pages we have described and illustrated some of the Pines most frequently planted for ornamental uses. Almost without exception Pines are trees which thrive in plenty of light. They do not stand much shade. They do better in a light, sandy or gravelly soil.

Foliage of Austrian Pine about one-half natural size.

249

Red or Norway Pine

distributed in North America. At one time it grew extensively throughout the lake states of Michigan, Wisconsin, and Minnesota; from there it extends both east and west through southern Canada.

Swiss Stone Pine (Pinus cembra)

This is an alpine plant from the mountains of northern Europe. It grows in a pyramidal form, rather slowly. It has five leaves in each cluster, somewhat darker and heavier than the White Pine. Its habit frequently is very narrow as compared to other Pines, making it valuable for small spaces. It reaches a considerable size in its native stands, but is among the smaller Pines in its cultivated state.

RED OR NORWAY PINE

(Pinus resinosa)

This is one of the leading northern-forest timber Evergreens, ranging second only to the White Pine in commercial value and in size.

It is a two-leafed species, named Red Pine, no doubt, because of the reddish color of the bark. It adapts itself readily to various soil and planting conditions. The peculiar characteristic of the Red Pine is the position of the needles, which are generally in clusters at the ends of the branches, giving it an appearance somewhat different from other Pines. It is a tall, massive-growing tree, rather broad, with a large head, when matured in cultivation. It is widely-

Swiss Stone Pine

LIMBER PINE (Pinus flexilis)

This tree somewhat resembles the White Pine, but, while the leaves are somewhat of the same appearance, with five in a cluster, they are longer and more compact. It has a peculiar characteristic of twisting each group of leaves in a different direction. This peculiarity gives it an appearance unlike other Pines. It is a native of the lower altitudes of the Rocky Mountains, extending north into southern Canada. It was brought into cultivation about 1860. The branches are of extreme flexibility, and may be bent almost double without breaking. Normally the foliage is dark green, although many trees have a bluish cast.

WESTERN YELLOW PINE (Pinus ponderosa)

Like some of the other American Evergreens, this tree exists in a rather widely-separated area, which fact really divides it into two distinct trees—one, the *Pinus ponderosa* of the Pacific Coast; the other, a sort sometimes designated as *Pinus ponderosa scopulorum,* a tree which extends from the Rocky Mountains considerable distance eastward. The type of *Pinus ponderosa* which is adapted to conditions in the middle west is, of course, the Rocky Mountain variety. It is a straight-trunked tree with long, heavy needles, which are the coarsest of any of the Pines which are commonly seen in the Northern states.

JAPANESE BLACK PINE (Pinus thunbergi)

This tree and its close relative, the Japanese Red Pine, are the species which are most frequently chosen by the Japanese for their dwarfing and distorting of trees. The Japanese Black Pine has whitish buds and its leaves are stiff and short. Its greatest value for planting lies in its adaptability to exposed conditions at the seashore. The tree shown in the picture had been growing ten years on Nantucket Island when this photograph was taken. It is named in honor of the Swedish botanist, Carl Thunberg, who spent several months in Japan as part of a five-year voyage collecting such trees and plants as he could find, about the year 1775.

Japanese Black Pine

HILL'S MUGHO PINE

The white tips show the new growth. This appearance is given the trees in late May and early June.

Hill Mugho Pine (Pinus Mughus)

This is one of the most extensively-used dwarf Evergreens. It is a native tree in the mountainous sections of northern Europe, where it shows a great variation in its growing habit, due, no doubt, to environment and altitude. A selected type, which might be considered as a horticultural variety, is the Hill Mugho Pine, the subject of the illustration above. This selected type is grown from seed collected in high altitudes in a most remote region in the borderland of western Germany. Its growth is compact, with numerous stems which extend out from the base of the tree and then ascend upwards, making it more in the nature of a low bush.

The development of the new season's growth, which is shown in the above picture, gives it the frequently-applied name, the Candle Pine.

By frequent trimming, trees may be maintained in a limited area and at a small size for a number of years. The trees which are shown in the bed planting on the opposite page were kept at approximately this size for over ten years. It has many uses in landscaping work, particularly in foundation groups, in rock gardens, and in any location where a tree of great vitality and hardiness and dwarf form is needed.

This specimen growing in Western New York, shows about the ultimate development under ideal growing conditions.

There are some other horticultural varieties of this tree offered by nurseries, with more open growth and more upright habit. The variety pictured here is by far the most valuable one for ornamental uses. There is an old definition of this tree which fits it perfectly—"short and stout and round about." The specimen shown at the top of page is, of course, a most unusual one. Many years of ideal growing conditions are required for a tree to develop to this size.

HILL'S MUGHO PINE IN BED PLANTING

Austrian Pine (Pinus nigra)

The one Pine which unquestionably stands in greatest favor, at least in the Middle West, is the Austrian Pine. Few trees show such remarkable resistance to the trying condition of city planting. Gas and smoky atmosphere have little effect on its growth. It also proves very satisfactory for seashore planting.

It has such a rich, deep, green color that it is known in some parts of Europe as the Black Pine. The needles are two in a sheath, straight and slender, and four to five inches long.

In older trees which are planted in the open the branch spread often nearly equals the height, but in its native forests of Europe it is a tree of considerable size, of eighty to one hundred twenty feet.

Josiah Hoopes, American nurseryman and horticulturist, wrote in 1867 as follows: "This valuable tree, although of comparatively recent origin, being unknown previous to the year 1835, has gradually worked itself into public favor, until at the present time it ranks as one of the most popular species and one of the few well-known Pines that are extensively planted. The numerous, rough branches are placed regularly around the tree and impart a massive appearance. The rather long, rigid, dark, green leaves are remarkably beautiful when viewed from a distance. It also adapts itself to almost every soil and situation, but prefers a rich, light loam, with a well drained subsoil and in such grows rapidly, and speedily forms a tree. Taking into account its rapidity of growth and the certainty with which it will speedily produce an effect, and owing also, in a great measure, to the peculiar prominence of its general outline, we consider it unrivalled."

Foliage of the Austrian Pine.

The passing years have failed to diminish in any way the enthusiasm of American planters for this fine Evergreen. It has for many years surpassed all other Pines of the upright growing type in number of trees sold in leading Evergreen nurseries.

It is still regarded by a great many authorities as a geographical variety of Pinus laricio (Corsican Pine), but in the United States, at least, it is seldom referred to under that name.

There are quite a number of horticultural varieties of it, including several dwarf forms.

Austrian Pine

Scotch Pine
(Pinus sylvestris)

This Pine is said to have greater geographical distribution than any other Pine, as it is spread over almost the whole of Europe and into Asia. There are numerous geographical variations, many of which have been named and cultivated, making it necessary to specify the origin of the seed in order to insure trees of any desired type.

In its native forest it ranges up to one hundred feet, but in cultivation is rather a small tree. Young trees are usually formal in outline, with a straight stem, branching regularly. In old age, with the loss of lower branches and the top branches increasing in size, it forms a flat, irregular growth. This gives the tree a very picturesque outline. In old specimens the bark may be described as cinnamon-brown or reddish, a characteristic which quite easily distinguishes this tree from the other Pines.

It is useful for wastelands, as it grows well on dry, sandy soil where many other Pines cannot survive. The leaves are about three inches long, twisting into a loose spiral, and giving it a rather odd appearance.

It is the best known Evergreen of the British Isles, where it formerly grew in a native state in Scotland. Here it is called "Scots Pine" or "Scots Fir."

This tree has been planted in the United States for a great many years and is a familiar sight throughout the great central west, both in villages and around farm homes. There are many horticultural varieties of it.

Doubtless, one important reason why this tree has been so widely planted is the unusual rapidity of growth. In this respect it ranks first among the Pines which grow in the vicinity of northern Illinois, at least.

Jack Pine

Jack Pine
(Pinus banksiana)

The natural range of this fast growing Pine extends from northwestern Canada in a broad belt, taking in northern Minnesota, Wisconsin and Michigan, and extending to the eastern seaboard. While it is not among the best of the ornamental sorts, it is, nevertheless, a valuable tree, one which will stand planting in barren sand, giving tree life to those localities which have great difficulty in establishing trees. In certain parts of Kansas and Nebraska it has been extensively used in the wastelands. This is not among the largest of the Pines. It varies in its stature according to the locality, from twenty-five to fifty feet, or perhaps more.

It takes its botanical name from Sir Joseph Banks, an English patron of horticulture in the last century.

Scotch Pine

WHITE PINE (Pinus strobus)

The best-known and most valuable, commercially, of all Pines of the northern forest is the White Pine. It has soft, pale-green leaves, borne in clusters of five. It is a very rapid grower, and eventually becomes the largest of all the Pines which thrive in the middle west. It formerly was the most valuable timber tree throughout the forest area of Wisconsin, Minnesota, and Michigan.

JAPANESE UMBRELLA PINE (Pinus densiflora umbraculifera)

This is the same tree that has been extensively known as Japanese Table Pine (*Pinus tanyosho*). It grows with a short, thick stem and a flat top, an ideal subject for rock gardens. This specimen, on the grounds of the Hill Nursery, was approximately three feet in diameter when the photograph was made.

OTHER PINES

There are so many other species of Pines which deserve a brief word of description that it is difficult to choose. Our purpose, however, in preparing this material is to give information concerning the Pines which are most frequently seen and most important in the central-western section of the country.

There are a number of valuable and interesting species of Pines native to the Pacific slope, none of which are dependable in this locality, but some of which are planted in the eastern states. On the opposite page we have shown in color an illustration of the foliage and cones of the Sugar Pine (*Pinus lambertiana*), a tree which bears the largest cone of any Evergreen. These cones frequently run up to twenty inches in length, the average being twelve inches, and three to four inches in diameter. This tree reaches up to two hundred feet in its native stands on the mountain slopes of Oregon and extending down the coast in California, where it forms a part of great forests. It is frequently planted in New England and the Atlantic coast states.

A familiar Pine, found growing naturally from New York to Florida and extending throughout the southern states to Texas, is the Shortleaved or Yellow Pine (*Pinus echinata*). This, however, is not an important ornamental tree.

The Jersey Pine (*Pinus virginiana*) is a rather small specimen, averaging twenty-five to thirty feet high, frequently found extending from New Jersey through Maryland, Virginia and most of the southern states up to the Mississippi River.

Familiar to persons living in the south, is the Longleaf Pine (*Pinus palustris*). This, however, is of more importance commercially than as an ornamental tree. Its very long needles, which range up to eighteen inches in length, are frequently found in northern shops where they are sent in large quantities for decorative purposes.

Another of the valuable Pacific Coast Pines is the Coulter Pine (*Pinus coulteri*). This tree, extending not so far north as the Sugar Pine, is of lesser hardiness and not extensively planted except in some of the southern states.

Mention should also be made of the Nut Pines, particularly the Pinyon (*Pinus edulis*). While this tree is not frequently used as an ornamental tree, it is valuable as a source of edible seeds or nuts. It inhabits a rather extensive mountainous area of Colorado, New Mexico, Utah, and Arizona.

An alphabetical list of many other Pines, which neither space nor interest permits us to offer in detailed description, will be found on pages fifty-two to fifty-four of this book.

FOLIAGE AND CONE OF THE FAMOUS SUGAR PINE
(Pinus lambertiana)

The illustration is one-third natural size. This picture is a reproduction from Volume one of Lawson's Pinetum Britannicum, a most exhaustive work on the subject of Conifers, published in England about fifty years ago.

CHAPTER XLVIII

The Yews (Taxus)

THE Yews comprise an extensive family generally included among the conifers, but differing from the Pines in the botanical structure of their flowers. The term "Pine," which includes many genera of Pines, Spruces, Firs, etc., is applied to trees which produce both the male and female flowers on the same tree. The Yew, on the other hand, produces the male flowers on one tree and the female flowers on another tree. The fruit is in the form of a soft, pulpy, scarlet, cup-shaped berry. An illustration of this Yew berry is shown on page 67.

There is some difference of opinion among scientific authorities as to the exact status of the various species of the Yew. By some well-known botanists, the Yew family is regarded as composed of a single species, the numerous, commonly-recognized species being but geographical variations of the same tree. The preponderance of opinion, however, seems to favor the system of classifying the Yew into at least seven species. Four of these are found in North America; one, in Europe; two, in eastern Asia. Only one of the American species, a low bush, the American Yew (*Taxus canadensis*), a species which inhabits an extensive area in the northern forests of the United States, is of any importance as an ornamental tree. The other American species are scarcely known or mentioned, being confined to small localities in Florida, in the Far West, and in Mexico.

The Japanese species (*Taxus cuspidata*), together with it numerous horticultural varieties, compose the one family of Yews best adapted to the United States. The English Yew (*Taxus baccata*), which also includes a great number of horticultural varieties and possibly hybrids, is extensively planted in the eastern states, it not being of satisfactory hardiness in the Middle West. While the Japanese Yew has long been regarded as one of our finest Evergreens, it is only within a past decade or two that it has been used extensively. As trees become available in larger quantities at lower costs, they will, without question, replace many species and varieties of other Evergreens of similar type.

The Yew has been for so many hundreds of years a cultivated plant that its botanical name *Taxus* is the identical name used by the Romans, who planted Yew extensively in their gardens.

The Yew is rich in folklore and legend, particularly in England, where it is one of the common sights of the countryside. Before the invention of firearms, when armies were equipped with bows and arrows, the Yew furnished the wood for the bows.

Likewise, on the other side of the world, the Japanese race has always held the Yew tree in high regard and has planted it around their temples and gardens for hundreds of years.

The Yew thrives in the shade, in this respect being different than most other Evergreens. The foliage is lush, rich, dark green and waxy. Some varieties grow slowly, and in general the impression exists that the Yew is of very slow growth. The fact is, however, that some Yews grow very rapidly; as rapidly, in fact, as many other genera of Evergreens. They are very heavy feeders and respond to fertilizing.

In landscape use they serve a wide variety of needs, being ideal for hedges, for formal effects, for foundation plantings, for rockeries and, in fact, for any landscape requirement where trees are needed which are of small dimensions as compared to many of the larger growing genera of Evergreens.

Closely allied to the Yews are a number of other genera, none of which are described in these pages; namely: *Cephalotaxus, Podocarpus, Phyllocladus, Saxegothaea,* and *Torreya.* Some of these genera grow in the United States, but only in the warmer sections.

Yew trees are particularly difficult to identify. Unless one is in daily contact with them, they can scarcely be told one from another, except of course, those sorts which have some outstanding characteristic of growing habit.

Within the life of one Yew, empires rise and fall. A span of three thousand years is credited to one Ancient Yew which was cut down in England some years ago.

"The Pine loves the hills,
   The Yew tree the north wind and
     the cold."

Thus wrote Virgil two thousand years ago. Yew trees are one of the oldest of Evergreens geologically. Fossils have been excavated from beneath the English Channel, which fact gives evidence that ancestors of the Yew flourished millions of years ago.

The wood of English bows;
   So men who are free
   Love the old yew-tree,
And the land where the yew-tree grows."
                  DOYLE.

Foliage of berries of Japanese Yew one-half natural size.

Japanese Yew

JAPANESE YEW (Taxus cuspidata)

In the words of the late Ernest H. Wilson it was "an auspicious day for American gardens, when, in 1861, Dr. George K. Hall introduced from Japan, *Taxus cuspidata,* which has proved perfectly immune to the worst winters this country has since known."

A bulletin of the Arnold Arboretum, states, "The Japanese Yew, for ornamental purposes, is the most useful narrow-leaved Evergreen for the climate of New England. In the Yew the younger green leaves are often tinged with yellowish bronze in a delightful contrast with the black-green of the older foliage. No matter what season of the year it is examined, it will be found a thing of beauty."

There are two distinct forms of the tree commonly known under the name of *Taxus cuspidata.* One, propagated from seed, develops a single stem, in most cases, and grows in an upright, symmetrical, branched tree as shown in the picture on this page, and in the colored picture of a small nursery tree on opposite page. This form is generally called *Taxus cuspidata capitata.*

The other form, grown from cuttings, develops into a spreading, bush shape, as illustrated at the bottom of page 270. Both of these trees are of equal hardiness, but, of course, they serve different purposes in landscaping.

This upright form is known to reach a height of fifty feet in its native country, although specimens of such size are not to be found anywhere in the United States.

The first introduction of the Japanese Yew to the outside world was made by Robert Fortune about 1855, when he sent it to England. A few years later it found its way to the United States.

The Yew is one of the few Evergreens well suited to planting in congested cities, as it survives the smoky and dusty atmosphere of city plantings.

There are several horticultural varieties of this tree, some of which are described in the following pages. The greater number of horticultural varieties of the Yew, which exist, are forms of the *Taxus baccata,* or English Yew. There are also some forms said to be hybrids, mention of which is also made in this chapter. Like the other Yews, the Japanese Yew thrives in the shade, and, although it will grow in the full sun, it has the peculiar ability to remain in a thrifty, healthy condition when the shade is quite heavy.

Japanese Yew

Hick's Yew

HICK'S YEW
(Taxus media hicksi)

This tree is regarded by some authorities as belonging to a separate species, *Taxus media,* thought to be a hybrid between *Taxus cuspidata* and *Taxus baccata.* However, it appears in all respects to be a form of the Japanese species, and, according to the Hick's Nursery, who introduced it, it is but a horticultural form of *Taxus cuspidata,* found growing many years ago in the Dana Arboretum, at Glencove, Long Island. It is a most unusual and valuable addition to the Yew family.

The numerous branches ascend almost vertically, although it makes a main stem. The color is a rich, dark, glossy green, and the habit very narrow and columnar.

The original tree is now said to be about fifteen feet tall and quite narrow in diameter. This has proven to be a very hardy type. It has become very popular throughout the country in recent years.

INTERMEDIA YEW (Taxus intermedia)

Although this tree does not appear to have received any official horticultural recognition, it is, nevertheless, a widely-known form, grown in various nurseries throughout the eastern states. Regardless of what its actual status may be, either as a horticultural variety of *Taxus cuspidata,* a hybrid form, or a species,

Intermedia Yew

it is a distinct tree. It is low and bushy in outline, making a very noticeable increase in annual growth over the ordinary spreading type of the *Taxus cuspidata.*

It also comes out much earlier in its new growth in the spring, as much as a week or ten days, and this, of course, may account to some extent for the unusually fast growth which it makes.

Hatfield Yew (Taxus media hatfieldi)

On the Hunnewell Estate at Wellesly, Massachusetts, where many Yew trees were planted, their behavior was closely studied by Mr. T. D. Hatfield in charge of those grounds. He has been responsible for a number of contributions to the Yew family. The Hatfield Yew is a hybrid; that is, it has been grown from seeds, one parent of which was the *Taxus cuspidata,* and the other, the *Taxus baccata*. It is a vigorous grower of upright, compact, conical habit, with ascending branches. It has been known for about thirty-five years.

Brown's Yew (Taxus cuspidata browni)

This is another vase-shaped form, a very graceful type. It grows rapidly and has an exceptionally deep, green color. It is one of the newer forms of the Japanese Yew, a type which was selected by Mr. Brown of the Cottage Gardens, Queens, Long Island, New York, propagated and introduced from that nursery.

A very great number of other horticultural forms of the Japanese Yew exist, many of them worthy of propagation, but so extensive in number and many of them so similar in habit of growth, that any attempt to completely classify and describe them is beyond the scope of the brief space which we can allow for the Yews.

Anderson Yew (Taxus cuspidata andersoni)

This tree is a selected form of the *Taxus cuspidata,* extensively grown in some of the eastern nurseries, a rather new type, as it is not as yet officially recorded or described in any of the books of reference on Evergreens. A picture of an immature specimen in the nursery is shown below.

Anderson Yew　　　　*Brown's Yew*　　　　*Hatfield Yew*

American Yew

"In the hollow of a Yew tree do they bow their heads in prayer!" One of the most curious of cemetery chapels in the world is the one built in the hollow of a Yew tree, more than five hundred years old, located in the Cemetery of Haie-de-Roulat, Department Eure, France. No doubt this tree is of the Taxus baccata or English Yew species. "P & A Photos."

AMERICAN YEW
(Taxus canadensis)

This is one of the few native American forms of Yew. It makes a low, rather straggly, spreading bush. It is rather easily burned by the winter sun and has quite generally been replaced in plantings within recent years by the more desirable Japanese forms. However, under favorable planting conditions, it is a tree worthy of being planted. This tree is known in some localities as ground Hemlock. It is found on moist and shaded sides of hills throughout a large section of the northern part of the United States and southern Canada. While it is more irregular in growth in a wild state, it has a more refined appearance when in cultivation. It may be trimmed and maintained in various forms. The winter color is much less desirable than in the Japanese species.

English Yew

English Yew
(Taxus baccata)

If this description of the Yews were being written for the information of planters in warmer sections of this country, we would feel obliged to devote an extensive description to the English Yew (*Taxus baccata*). This tree is very famed throughout England and Europe, where it has been used as an ornamental tree for many hundreds of years. As a result, there are almost hundreds of horticultural varieties of many conceivable characteristics of color, shape, and foliage variation. However, neither the English Yew nor any of its numerous forms are grown satisfactorily in the central western states. They are quite extensively planted in the vicinity of New York and somewhat up into New England, where they have the disadvantage of frequent winter injury.

The typical form of this native species is a tree twenty-five feet up to sixty feet, although generally the growth is rambling. The trees have an immense trunk, broken up into numerous branches.

Irish Yew
(Taxus baccata fastigiata)

It has an upright, fastigiate, type of growth. There have been forms of this tree selected and propagated in the last one hundred years. The tree shown in the picture is 105 years old, growing on Long Island.

Irish Yew

Dwarf Japanese Yew

Dwarf Japanese Yew
(Taxus cuspidata nana)

This is the slowest-growing of the Yews. Its branches are covered with little bunches of blackish-green foliage, retaining its color well throughout the season. It is one of the oldest horticultural forms of the Japanese Yew. It fills a unique place among the Evergreens, having a low, irregular, and picturesque outline. Old specimens of it bear a closer resemblance to Boxwood than any other Evergreen.

At the famous Highland Park in Rochester, New York, are specimens of this tree more than thirty-five years old, some of which are fifteen to sixteen feet in diameter, and about five feet tall.

By occasional trimming, the tree may be kept much smaller, and it therefore makes one of the most ideal Evergreens for rock gardens and other areas where trees of unusually slow growth or dwarf form are necessary.

Japanese Yew—Spreading Type (Taxus cuspidata)

The picture below shows a specimen of the Japanese Yew described at length on page 265. This is the form grown from cuttings, which produces a low, spreading bush.

Japanese Yew—Spreading type

Dwarf Japanese Yew

This grotesque display of topiary work in an old English garden is fashioned from the English Yew. Illustration from Veitch's Manual of the Coniferae

CHAPTER XLIX

Arborvitae (Thuya)

THE flat, lacy foliage of the Arborvitae is familiar to everyone. It has no resemblance to the foliage of Pines, Spruces, or Firs, but looks somewhat like the foliage of some of the Cypress and Junipers.

The family of Arborvitae which are in cultivation are composed of but five species. There are one or two other obscure Asiatic species not of sufficient interest for ornamental use, or at least very little known.

Two species of the Arborvitae are native to North America. The American Arborvitae (*Thuya occidentalis*) is spread in its natural range over a very extensive area from Nova Scotia on the east, clear across southern Canada and the northern section of the United States to Minnesota. The other American species is the Giant Arborvitae (*Thuya plicata*), sometimes called the Western Arborvitae, which extends from Alaska down into California, and eastward to the Rocky Mountains.

There are two or three Asiatic species found in China, Japan, and Korea, the most important one being the Chinese Arborvitae (*Thuya orientalis*). This is a species which has long been cultivated in the United States, throughout the southern states, as well as in many other localities of temperate climate in this country. Like the American Arborvitae, it has a large number of horticultural varieties.

The Latin name Arborvitae, meaning "Tree of Life," was applied to this family more than three hundred years ago when it was first brought to Europe. As to why this name was applied, there is no record.

With their single directness, the American Indians called the Arborvitae "Featherleaf," a term aptly descriptive of the lacy, feathery foliage.

Arborvitae is a valuable source of timber and, as such, is generally known under the name of White Cedar. Many of the telegraph and telephone poles are Arborvitae.

Foliage of American Arborvitae one-half natural size.

A specimen of American Arborvitae photographed in the Hill Nursery. This tree was about five feet tall. Its form is typical of smaller trees. Arborvitae make excellent hedges and may be trimmed either into low or tall hedges.

AMERICAN ARBORVITAE (Thuya occidentalis)

The American Arborvitae was one of the first American trees introduced to Europe. Records differ somewhat as to the exact date, but it was quite evidently introduced into Germany about 1550, and was well enough known in England to be included by Gerard in his "Historie of Plants" published in 1597. It is most variable when grown from seed. This, together with the fact that it has been so long in cultivation, accounts for the great abundance of horticultural varieties of it. As the Arborvitae is of more or less small stature in cultivation, being extensively used for ornamental or landscape purposes, it is natural that so many of these horticultural varieties have been developed. On page 57 of this book is a list of more than fifty of the best known of the horticultural forms of the American Arborvitae. There are, no doubt, others.

Nurseries frequently trim the American Arborvitae into compact specimens when they are offered for sale, so that small plants are very attractive.

The great majority of Evergreen hedges which have been planted throughout the middle western states during the last fifty to seventy-five years are of the American Arborvitae. This tree is one of the commonest sights around country homes and in the villages of the great middle-western section of this country. It is also extensively planted in all the states extending to the east coast, but in the southern section of the country, as well as in the far west, it is largely replaced with the Chinese Arborvitae.

A group of American Arborvitae as they grow in their natural surroundings.

George Peabody Arborvitae
(Thuya occidentalis lutea)

This tree is one of the oldest of the golden forms. The foliage is light green, with bright, golden tips. In this section, at least, it is the brightest-golden color of all the Arborvitae.

It is rather pyramidal in habit, with ascending branchlets, and grows up to twenty feet or more in height.

George Peabody Arborvitae

Douglas Golden Arborvitae

Douglas Golden Arborvitae
(Thuya occidentalis douglassi aurea)

This tree is a bronzy yellow during the late spring and summer, darkening a little during the winter. It is vigorous-growing, broad and pyramidal in growth. While it is not so bright in color as the George Peabody Arborvitae, it is a more vigorous grower.

It reaches a considerable breadth and height and is, therefore, of great value in adding color contrasts to a planting of darker green trees. It has been in cultivation for a great many years.

Parsons Compact Arborvitae
(Thuya occidentalis compacta)

A very old form of dwarf and compact habit. It originated in the Parsons Nursery at Flushing, Long Island, many years ago. Murray Hornibrook in his book, "Dwarf and Slow Growing Conifers," describes it as follows: "Possibly the best known of the dwarf forms. A compact ball of fresh green foliage; branchlets crowded and somewhat twisted. Short and stout. Ultimate growth about five feet in diameter, the branchlet sprays being about three inches long by four inches across."

Douglas Pyramidal Arborvitae
(Thuya occidentalis douglassi pyramidalis)

The foliage of this interesting variety is short, dense, dark green and is arranged in small curled or twisted clusters resembling a cock's comb. In habit of growth it is very narrow; a fact which, because of its tall growth, makes it a good substitute in northern localities for the Italian Cypress. It keeps its winter

Douglas Pyramidal Arborvitae

Parsons Compact Arborvitae

color much better than most other Arborvitaes. Another form often listed as *Thuya occidentalis spiralis,* if not the same tree, is very similar.

LITTLE GEM ARBORVITAE
(Thuya occidentalis little gem) (pumila)

Nowhere in the great family of Evergreens will one find more confusion of description and names than among the Arborvitaes. This is, of course, natural when we realize that this tree has been grown for so many hundreds of years by nurseries in various parts of the world. Sometimes trees of entirely different characters have been disseminated under identical names. Other nurseries not so conscientious perhaps, have sold almost any dwarf tree under a name which has some established reputation. Just where the tree known as "Little Gem" originated we do not know. This picture of a small tree in the Hill Nursery gives some idea of the unusual fineness of the foliage and the extremely dwarf, compact habit of its growth. It is one of two or three true dwarf forms among the Arborvitae, a tree which is well suited for planting in a rock garden. The growth is very slow, and the color is somewhat deeper and richer green than in the American Arborvitae. In Bailey's "The Cultivated Conifers" this tree is described as "an admirable low form, which in thirty-five years did not exceed two and one-half feet in height and forms a spreading, low cushion, retaining a dark green color."

OTHER ARBORVITAES

Among the other Arborvitaes, which space does not allow us to illustrate, we wish to make brief mention of a few as follows:

Columbia Arborvitae and Queen Victoria Arborvitae. These are two upright growers, both having variegated white or silver foliage.

Threadleaf Arborvitae (*Thuya occidentalis filiformis*). This is an odd-looking form with slender, rather drooping, and long branchlet sprays. It bears close resemblance to the well known Thread Retinospora.

Vervaene Arborvitae (*Thuya occidentalis vervaeneana*). A yellowish-foliaged form, having a rather dull, bronze, winter color.

Cushion Arborvitae (*Thuya occidentalis umbraculifera*). An extremely dwarf form, having thin, fine, dark green foliage. It forms a low, cushion-shaped bush.

Rosenthal Arborvitae (*Thuya occidentalis rosenthali*). A pyramidal form with dark lustrous green foliage.

Recurva Nana Arborvitae (*Thuya occidentalis recurva nana*). Dwarf, globe-shaped, growing into a perfect ball.

Hovey Arborvitae (*Thuya occidentalis hoveyi*). This is another of the older, well-known dwarf Arborvitaes, which grows in a somewhat beehive shape with rather bright green foliage.

Little Gem Arborvitae

Tom Thumb Arborvitae
(Thuya occidentalis ellwangeriana)

Whoever named this form evidently sought to capitalize on the famous Tom Thumb midget, made famous by the great Barnum.

This is a rather broad pyramidal form, with an abundance of juvenile foliage scattered throughout the plant, giving it an appearance quite unlike the familiar Arborvitae foliage. In this respect it is a type rather midway between the typical American Arborvitae and the Heath Arborvitae (*Thuya occidentalis ericoides*), which is composed entirely of the juvenile foliage. Some older plants are as much as five to six feet high and almost as broad. It is named after George Ellwanger, one of the proprietors of the old Ellwanger and Barry Nursery.

Heath Arborvitae
(Thuya occidentalis ericoides)

This tree is so named because of its resemblance to the foliage of the Heath or Heather. The branchlets are slender, flexible, more or less upright, very dense and the leaves are entirely of the juvenile kind. That is, they are needle shaped, rather than having the flat spray of the typical Arborvitae.

Both of the above named varieties are, of course, of more value as curiosities than as ornamentals.

Tom Thumb Arborvitae

Heath Arborvitae

Pyramidal Arborvitae (Thuya occidentalis pyramidalis)

The one most widely-planted Arborvitae, and the variety of most value in landscaping among the many forms of the American Arborvitae, is, without question, the Pyramidal Arborvitae pictured on this page. It is a tree which grows with much more pyramidal and narrow habit than the American Arborvitae, and it has a richer, deeper color and more formal outline. Even old trees up to twenty-five feet or more have a diameter of only two or three feet at the base.

Woodward Arborvitae
(Thuya occidentalis woodwardi)

This globe form is one of the best and most widely known of the many globe-shaped Arborvitaes. It was originated and introduced many years ago by Mr. Manning, proprietor of the Reading Nurseries, Reading, Massachusetts, and named after his son, J. Woodward Manning. It assumes the natural globe form and, while it may reach to a considerable diameter, it continues to maintain a well-rounded shape. The foliage is dark green.

Pyramidal Arborvitae

Woodward Arborvitae

Ware Arborvitae

WARE ARBORVITAE (Thuya occidentalis wareana)

This old and well-known variety was raised by, and named for, Mr. Thomas Ware, an English Nurseryman, who produced it about 1850. A specimen reported by Mr. Arthur D. Slavin of Rochester, New York, was fifteen feet high and nine feet across at the base. This is a rather unusual specimen. It generally is much smaller in size. It is conical in outline and covered with dark green foliage, thicker and heavier than the American Arborvitae. It was originally named "Siberian Arborvitae" because of its rugged constitution and still is widely known under that name. It is also known under the name of *robutsa*.

Giant Western Arborvitae (Thuya plicata)

While it is a most important timber tree, this species is not so extensively planted for ornamental use. It is not as hardy as the American Arborvitae, at least in the central states. It covers an extensive area from California to Alaska and extends eastward to the Rocky Mountains. There is a noticeable difference in the hardiness of the trees from the Rocky Mountain region as compared to the trees from the moist, humid Pacific Coast region.

Giant Western Arborvitae

The branches are short, with rather slightly-nodding branchlets. Foliage is much larger than the other species of Arborvitae, with a noticeable, whitish marking below, bright green above. It has a plaited or rejointed appearance.

This tree reached England very early in the nineteenth century and has been greatly used and much appreciated there for the excellent quality of the tree, both for ornamental and timber purposes. Several trees in England have now reached one hundred feet or more in height. The wood is fragrant and of unusual lasting quality. In the forests, sound, fallen trunks have been found which have other large trees growing over them. An interesting account of this tree is found in "Gordon's Pinetum" in which he says, "The natives of Nootka Sound manufacture their cloaks of its inner bark, which turns the rain, is very pliable and soft, and is in use for mats, sails, ropes, clothing, etc."

There are but a few horticultural varieties of it. A pendulous or weeping form, var. *pendula;* a columnar form, var. *fastigiata;* and a form with wellow foliage, var. *aurea.*

The photograph is a specimen in Highland Park Pinetum, Rochester, N. Y.

CHINESE ARBORVITAE

(Thuya orientalis)

This is a most important species of Arborvitae throughout a large part of the United States where the climate is not too severe. It is widely used on the Pacific Coast and throughout the southern states. Occasionally plants of it or its varieties are found in northern Illinois, but it is not a dependable tree in this vicinity.

The late Ernest Wilson in his book, "Conifers and Taxads of Japan" states, "Its range as a wild plant is not properly understood. It is known to be indigenous in Korea and north-eastern China and may have a wider range in that country."

It has been cultivated both as a species and in its many forms for a long period, being one of the first of the Asiatic trees distributed to America and Europe. Like the American Arborvitae, it is most variable when grown from seed. The photograph of the specimen on this page was grown from seed collected in Korea by Ernest Wilson, and now growing in Durand-Eastman Park, Rochester, New York. It shows a much better type of tree than the usual form.

The foliage of this species is generally finer and less heavy than the American Arborvitae. The tendency of some forms of it is to grow from numerous stems at the base rather than branching out in horizontal formation. An extensive list of its horticultural varieties, by no means complete, is found on page 58 of this book. In the following pages we have described a number of the leading sorts.

Chinese Arborvitae

Oriental Pyramidal Arborvitae

(Thuya orientalis pyramidalis)

This tree is a selected form, one of the older ornamental favorites growing in a compact, rather narrow, pyramidal shape. Other varieties growing in an upright habit, of which we wish to make brief mention, are the following:

Silver Oriental Arborvitae (*Thuya orientalis argenteo variegata*). This form has creamy white tips.

The variety *beverleyensis,* a tree extensively planted particularly in California, is a columnar grower with golden yellow tips.

A tree which greatly resembles the Pyramidal Oriental Arborvitae pictured to the left, is the Goldspire Arborvitae (*Thuya orientalis aurea conspicua*). This is a great favorite, making a compact pyramidal tree with golden yellow foliage mixed with green. It is a particularly attractive tree when the new growth is coming out in the spring.

Another of the many golden forms, which is somewhat lower and wider in habit, is the variety *elegantissima*. The bright yellow foliage changes to yellowish green during the season.

Pyramidal Oriental Arborvitae

One old tree, which for many years puzzled horticulturists, who thought it to be a hybrid between the Red Cedar and Oriental Arborvitae is the variety *meldensis,* a form having all prickly or juvenile foliage as shown in the illustration of the small branch on this page.

Variety *bonita* is a broad, cone-shaped, bright green tree, rather slow-growing. A very popular variety.

A bluish type was introduced some years ago called var. *texana glauca.*

Foliage of Oriental Arborvitae var. Meldensis. A juvenile foliaged form.

Berckmann Golden Arborvitae (Thuya orientalis aurea nana)

By far the most widely-known and extensively planted of the horticultural varieties of the Oriental Arborvitae is this attractive little bright-yellow tree. It makes a neat, compact growth, thickly covered with attractive golden-colored foliage. It is a great favorite throughout the United States in localities where it thrives. It has the vertical, fan-shaped branch development with numerous stems growing upright, closely matted together.

Compacta Arborvitae

In growing habit it somewhat resembles the Berckmann's Golden form, although in color it is a bright, shiny green. The growth is very broad, tapering to a blunt pyramid. It is a great favorite for landscape work and foundation-plantings, and other situations requiring a tree of moderate size.

Rosedale Arborvitae

This form is not so well-known or widely-used, but it makes an interesting novelty in the peculiar growth which it makes. As shown in this small picture, the foliage of this tree is very fine and feathery, unlike the normal foliage of Arborvitae.

Compacta Arborvitae

Rosedale Arborvitae

Berckmann Arborvitae

CHAPTER L

Hemlock (Tsuga)

THIS is one of the smaller families of Evergreens, being composed of two species in the eastern part of North America, two in western North America, and some species in Japan and China. Almost all of the Hemlock in cultivation are confined to the Canada or American Hemlock (*Tsuga canadensis*), the Carolina Hemlock (*Tsuga caroliniana*), and one or two other slightly-used species. Hemlock were formerly included among the Firs and later under the Spruces. Even now the tree is quite commonly referred to as "Hemlock Spruce." However, for the past seventy-five years or more, Hemlocks have been commonly designated as a separate family of Evergreens. They are trees which have unusual grace, and pendulous, flowing branches. They are able to withstand considerable shade. They make ideal material for hedges.

While they are considered as a hardy family, growing to a considerable distance northward in the northern forests of the United States, they are not able to withstand severe exposure and as a family do better in a cool, moist soil and a partially protected spot. On the whole, they should be planted somewhat protected from the southern winter sun as they are quite easily burned.

American Hemlock (½ natural size)

Mention should be made here of the extensive collection of Hemlock which is being developed by Mr. Charles F. Jenkins at his Hemlock Arboretum near Philadelphia. He has, on his grounds, all the known varieties of Hemlock, as well as many interesting forms as yet unnamed, and not generally available in the nursery trade.

The American Hemlock thrives over a considerable area of the United States, being especially beautiful in the New England and eastern states and extending to Illinois and Wisconsin on the west.

American Hemlock

CANADA HEMLOCK OR AMERICAN HEMLOCK (Tsuga canadensis)

O Hemlock Tree! O Hemlock Tree! How faithful are thy branches.
Green not alone in summertime,
But in winter's frost and rime,
O Hemlock Tree! O Hemlock Tree! How faithful are thy branches.
—Longfellow

No more interesting account of this species of Hemlock is found anywhere than in the words of Josiah Hoopes in his "Book of Evergreens," written more than seventy years ago. He states: "The regular conical form, tapering from a broad base evenly to a long, straight, and thrifty leading shoot, is the common shape of this tree. The long, slender branches, drooping gracefully to the ground, present so beautiful a picture that it is indeed difficult to surpass it, and when we compare the rich, dark green foliage of a healthy plant that is varied so exquisitely with the marked glaucousness of the underside of the leaves, we must admire a tree which presents such a diversity of charms.

"A mistake is sometimes made by planting the Hemlock in dry situations, for, while it cannot thrive in wet and swampy ground, it greatly prefers a rather moist, deep, loamy soil and cool location, the better if partially shaded. In such spots the beauty of the foliage and the luxuriant growth speedily develop themselves to the highest degree."

As shown in the photograph below, the Hemlock makes one of the most beautiful and graceful hedges, and it has long been used in many localities for that purpose.

At the New York Botanical Garden in New York City there is a natural forest of these Hemlocks with specimens ranging up to ninety feet tall. The Arnold Arboretum is also noted for the trees on "Hemlock Hill," a natural forest growth of Hemlocks.

In cultivation, when planted by itself in the open, it seldom reaches more than twenty-five feet in height, with a spread of branches ten or twelve feet.

Hemlock trimmed into a hedge.

Carolina Hemlock
(Tsuga caroliniana)

An interesting light on the Carolina Hemlock is reported in Bulletin No. 4, July 1, 1933, of the Hemlock Arboretum: "For nearly a hundred years a long list of experienced botanists had combed the southern Alleghenies, beginning with William Bartram, Micheaux, the Frasers, and in 1842, Asa Gray himself. None of them had noted any difference in the Hemlocks which grew so profusely on crag and mountain and in glen and gorge. It was in 1858 that Prof. Lewis R. Gibbs reported to the Elliott Society of Charleston, S. C., a body formed for the serious study of natural history, as follows: "Professor Gibbs mentioned his recent verification of a suspicion he had entertained respecting the existence of a new specie of Fir in the Saluda Mountains, resembling American Hemlock, but clearly distinct by well-marked characteristics." Thus, to the distinguished scientist of Charleston, belongs the honor of discovering and identifying the charming Tsuga caroliniana."

According to Harlan P. Kelsey, to whom we are indebted for our picture and who is credited with having introduced this remarkable tree to cultivation, it is a specimen which ranges from thirty to seventy feet, much less in cultivation. It has dark, dense, tufted foliage on sweeping, pendulous branches. It was regarded by the late Professor Sargent as "The handsomest conifer we grow in New England." Unfortunately, this enthusiasm cannot be shared by planters in the Middle West, as this tree is not at home here in northern Illinois. It does, nevertheless, occupy a position of prominence among the Hemlocks and should be grown by anyone in a locality where it thrives.

Carolina Hemlock

Sargent Weeping Hemlock

JAPANESE HEMLOCK (Tsuga diversifolia)

This is an Asiatic representative of this interesting family. In cultivation it forms a rather low, bushy-growing tree with a number of stems, while in Japan it develops into a tree up to seventy-five feet in height. Although this tree is seldom, if ever, planted here in the middle western states, it is frequently seen and highly regarded in other localities, particularly in the East where it has proven itself hardy and of distinct character.

SARGENT WEEPING HEMLOCK (Tsuga canadensis pendula)

Japanese Hemlock

Doubtless the best-known horticultural variety of American Hemlock is the well-known Sargent Weeping Hemlock. This tree is named in honor of H. W. Sargent. It was found probably fifty years ago, growing wild in the Fishkill Mountains in New York State. The picture above well illustrates the most unusual character of the tree. It lies in a mass of closely-woven pendulous branchlets which droop to the ground.

Books on Evergreens

THE following list of books covers the most important ones printed in the English language on the subject of Evergreens. This list of books does not include those with subject matter made up largely of strictly technical botanical information, nor does this list cover numerous articles, many of which are highly important and interesting, and which have appeared in magazines and pamphlets. The list shows the year of publication, the name of the author, and the name of the book. Some of these volumes were very limited private editions, which are now scarce and valuable.

1832	Aylmer Bourke Lambert. "A Description of the Genus Pinus" (2 vol.)
1839	James Forbes. "Pinetum Woburnense"
1846	J. G. Zuccarini. "Morphology of the Coniferae"
1850	Joseph Knight and Thomas A. Perry. "Synopsis of the Coniferous Plants Grown in Great Britain"
1855	Andrew Murray. "Description of New Coniferous Trees from California"
1858	George Gordon and Robert Glendinning. "The Pinetum; Being a Synopsis of All the Coniferous Plants at Present Known"
1862	George Gordon. "A Supplement to Gordon's Pinetum"
1863	George Engelmann. "On Pinus Aristata and Some Other Pines of the Rocky Mountains"
1863	Andrew Murray. "The Pines and Firs of Japan"
1863–84	James Edward Ravenscroft. "The Pinetum Britannicum" (3 vol.)
1866	"Senilis" (i.e. John Nelson) "Pinaceae: Being a Handbook of the Firs and Pines"
1868	Robert Brown of Campster. "Monograph of the Coniferous Genus Thuja Linn., and of the North American Species of the Genus Libocedrus Endl.
1868	Josiah Hoopes. "The Book of Evergreens; A Practical Treatise on the Coniferae, or Cone-Bearing Plants"
1868	Thomas Meehan. "Variations in Taxodium and Pinus"
1869	Robert Hutchison. "The Cultivation of the Newer Coniferae, with Special Reference to the Climate of Great Britain and Ireland"
1875	Hugh Fraser. "Handy Book of Ornamental Conifers, etc."
1875	George Gordon. "The Pinetum" (2nd ed.)
1876	William Ramsay M'Nab. "A Revision of the Species of Abies"
1877	George Engelmann. "The American Junipers of the Section Sabina"
1878	George Engelmann. "A Synopsis of the American Firs Abies"
1880	George Engelmann. "Revision of the Genus Pinus"
1880	George Gordon. "The Pinetum" (New ed.)
1881	Maxwell Tylden Masters. "The Conifers of Japan"
1881	James Veitch & Sons. "A Manual of the Coniferae"
1886	M. T. Masters. "Contributions to the History of Certain Species of Conifers"
1892	Royal Horticultural Society. "Report of the Conifer Conference"
1893	M. T. Masters. "The Genera of Taxaceae and Coniferae"

1896   A. D. Webster. "Hardy Coniferous Trees"
1897   John Lowe. "The Yew Trees of Great Britain and Ireland"
1900   John Gill Lemmon. "Handbook of West-American Cone-Bearers"
1900   James Veitch & Sons. "Veitch's Manual of the Coniferae" (New ed.)
1901   M. T. Masters. "Hybrid Conifers"
1902   M. T. Masters. "Coniferae"
1904   M. T. Masters. "A General View of the Genus Pinus"
1905   Charles Sprague Sargent. "The Pinetum at Wellesley, Mass."
1906   M. T. Masters. "The Conifers of China"
1909   George Russell Shaw. "The Pines of Mexico"
1909–13 H. Clinton-Baker. "Illustrations of Conifers" (3 vol.)
1910   Richard T. Baker and Henry G. Smith. "A Research on the Pines of Australia"
1914   George Russell Shaw. "The Genus Pinus"
1916   Ernest Henry Wilson. "The Conifers and Taxads of Japan"
1918   A. D. Webster. "Coniferous Trees for Profit and Ornament"
1920   Charles Coltman-Rogers. "Conifers and Their Characteristics"
1923   L. H. Bailey. "The Cultivated Evergreens"
1923   W. Dallimore and A. Bruce Jackson. "A Handbook of Coniferae Including Ginkgoaceae"
1923   Murray Hornibrook. "Dwarf and Slow-Growing Conifers"
1927   John Davidson. "Conifers, Junipers and Yew: Gymnosperms of British Columbia"
1927   U. S. Dept. of Agriculture Bulletin No. 460. "The Pine Trees of the Rocky Mountain Region"
1932   Royal Horticultural Society. "Conifers in Cultivation"
1933   L. H. Bailey. "The Cultivated Conifers"

Index